Head Start to A-Level Physics

A-Level Physics is a **big step up** from GCSE... no doubt about that.
But don't worry — this CGP book has been lovingly made to help you
hit the ground running at the start of your A-Level (or AS-Level) course.

It recaps everything you'll need to remember from GCSE, and introduces
some of the crucial concepts you'll meet at A-Level. For every topic, there are
crystal-clear study notes and plenty of **practice questions** to test your skills.

What CGP is all about

Our sole aim here at CGP is to produce the highest quality books
— carefully written, immaculately presented and dangerously
close to being funny.

Then we work our socks off to get them out to you
— at the cheapest possible prices.

Contents

Section 4 — Electricity

Section 5 — Waves

Section 6 — Atoms and Radioactivity

Section 7 — Investigating and Interpreting

Published by CGP

Author:
Richard Tattersall

Editors:
David Maliphant
Rachael Marshall
Sam Pilgrim

ISBN: 978 1 78294 281 8

With thanks to Sarah Williams for the proofreading.
With thanks to Laura Jakubowski for the copyright research.

Clipart from Corel®
Printed by Elanders Ltd, Newcastle upon Tyne.

Based on the classic CGP style created by Richard Parsons.

Symbols and Units

At A-Level, you're expected to use **standard scientific notation**. This means using **conventional symbols** and **units**, and writing very large and very small numbers in **standard form**.

The table below lists the different quantities you'll come across in this book, with their standard symbols and units:

Quantity	Symbol	Unit
Displacement (distance)	s	metre, m
Time	t	second, s
Velocity (speed)	v	metre per second, ms^{-1}
Acceleration	a	metre per second squared, ms^{-2}
Mass	m	kilogram, kg
Force	F	newton, N
Gravitational field strength	g	newton per kilogram, Nkg^{-1}
Energy	E	joule, J
Work	W	joule, J
Power	P	watt, W
Frequency	f	hertz, Hz
Wavelength	λ	metre, m
Charge	Q	coulomb, C
Electric current	I	ampere, A
Potential difference	V	volt, V
Resistance	R	ohm, Ω

At A-Level, units like m/s are written ms^{-1}.
This is just **index notation**.
(If it doesn't make sense to you, look up 'rules of indices' in a maths book.)

Standard form lets us write **very big** or **very small** numbers in a more convenient way. It looks like this:

A must be between 1 and 10 → $A \times 10^n$ ← *n* is the number of places the decimal point moves

For example:
53 100 can be written as **5.31×10^4**, and **2.5×10^{-3}** is the same as **0.0025**.

You might also see large or small numbers given in units with these prefixes:

Multiple	Prefix	Symbol
10^{12}	tera	T
10^9	giga	G
10^6	mega	M
10^3	kilo	k
10^{-2}	centi	c
10^{-3}	milli	m
10^{-6}	micro	μ
10^{-9}	nano	n
10^{-12}	pico	p
10^{-15}	femto	f

Make sure you give your answers to questions to a sensible number of **significant figures**.

An easy way to do this is by always rounding your answers to the **same number** of significant figures as the given data value you've used in the calculation with the **least** significant figures.

Then **write** the number of significant figures you've rounded your answer to:
e.g. $2 \div 3.5 = 0.571... =$ **0.6 (to 1 s.f.)**
(2 is to 1 s.f., 3.5 is to 2 s.f., so the answer needs to be given to 1 s.f.)

Speed, Displacement and Velocity

Distance, Time and Speed are all Related

Points A and B are separated by a **distance** in **metres**. Now imagine a spider walking from A to B — you can measure the **time** it takes, in **seconds**, for it to travel this distance.

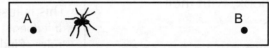

You can then work out the spider's **average speed** between A and B using this **equation**:

speed (in metres per second) = **distance travelled** (in metres) ÷ **time taken** (in seconds)

This is a very useful equation, but it does have a couple of **limitations**:

Well aren't you a cutie...

1) It only tells you the **average** speed. The spider could **vary** its speed from fast to slow and even go **backwards**. So long as it gets from A to B in the **same time** you get the **same answer**.

2) We assume that the spider takes the **shortest possible path** between the two points (a straight line), rather than **meandering** around.

Displacement is a Vector Quantity

To get from point A to point B you need to know what **direction** to travel in — just knowing the **distance** you need to travel **isn't enough**.

This information, **distance plus direction**, is known as the **displacement** from A to B and has the symbol **s**. It's a **vector** quantity — **all** vector quantities have both a **size** and a **direction**.

There is a Relationship Between Displacement and Velocity

Velocity is another **vector quantity** — velocity is the **speed** and **direction** of an object.
The **velocity** of an object is given by the following equation:

velocity (in metres per second) = **displacement** (in metres) ÷ **time taken** (in seconds)

Or, in symbols: $v = \dfrac{s}{t}$

This equation is very similar to the one relating **speed** and **distance**, except that it includes information about the **direction of motion**.

Displacement's in a relationship with velocity now, it's so over time...

1) An athlete runs a 1500 m race in a time of 210 seconds. What is his average speed?

2) The speed of light is 3.0×10^8 ms^{-1}. If it takes light from the Sun 8.3 minutes to reach us, what is the distance from the Earth to the Sun?

3) A snail crawls at a speed of 0.24 centimetres per second.
How long does it take the snail to travel 1.5 metres?

4) How long does it take a train travelling with a velocity of 50 ms^{-1} north to travel 1 km?

5) If someone has a velocity of 7.50 ms^{-1} south, what is their displacement after 15.0 seconds?

Drawing Displacements and Velocities

You can use *Scale Drawings* to *Represent Displacement*

The simplest way to draw a vector is to draw an **arrow**. So for a displacement vector the **length** of the arrow tells you the **distance**, and the way the arrow **points** shows you the **direction**.

A———————————————▶B

You can do this even for very large displacements so long as you **scale down**. Whenever you do a scale drawing, make sure you **state the scale** you are using.

EXAMPLE: Draw arrows to scale to represent a displacement of 3 metres upwards and a displacement of 7 metres to the right.

A displacement of 3 metres upwards could be represented by an arrow of length 3 centimetres.

Using this same scale (1 cm to 1 m) a displacement of 7 metres to the right would be an arrow of length 7 centimetres.

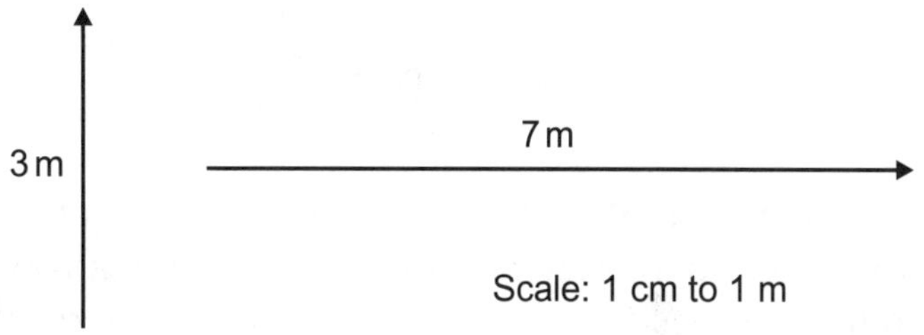

3m

7 m

Scale: 1 cm to 1 m

You can also *Represent Velocities* with *Arrows*

Velocity is a **vector**, so you can **draw arrows** to show velocities too. This time, the **longer** the **arrow**, the **greater** the **speed** of the object. A typical scale might be 1 cm to 1 ms⁻¹.

EXAMPLE: Draw arrows to scale to represent velocities of 5 metres per second to the right and 3 metres per second downwards.

Draw the velocities like this with a scale of 1 cm to 1 ms⁻¹:

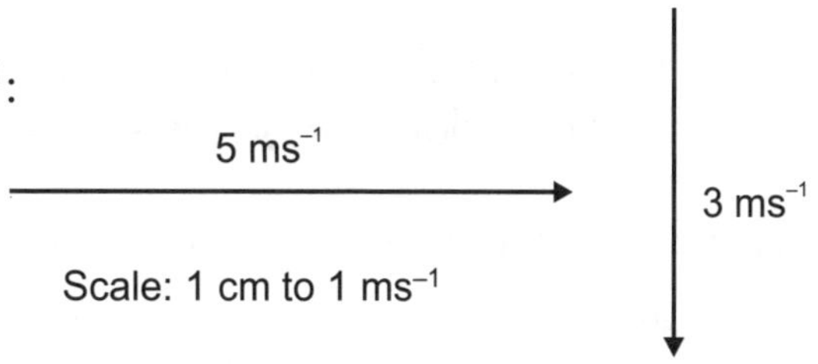

5 ms⁻¹

3 ms⁻¹

Scale: 1 cm to 1 ms⁻¹

Drawing displacements — not about leaving your sketchbook at home...

1) Draw arrows representing the following displacements to the given scale:
   a) 12 m to the right (1 cm to 2 m)
   b) 110 miles at a bearing of 270° (1 cm to 20 miles)
2) Draw an arrow to represent each velocity to the given scale. Take north to be up the page.
   a) 60 ms⁻¹ to the south-east (1 cm to 15 ms⁻¹)
   b) 120 miles per hour to the west (1 cm to 30 miles per hour)

Combining Displacements and Velocities

To **add** two velocity or displacement vectors, you **can't** simply add together the two distances as this doesn't account for the **different directions** of the vectors. What you do is:

1) **Draw** arrows representing the two vectors.
2) **Place** the arrows **one after the other** "tip-to-tail".
3) Draw a **third** arrow from start to finish. This is your **resultant vector**.

EXAMPLE: Add a displacement of 4 metres on a bearing of 090° to a displacement of 3 metres on a bearing of 060°. Use a scale of 1 cm to 1 m.

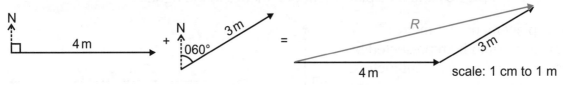

R is the **resultant** vector— it's the sum of the two displacements.
You can find the size of R by measuring the arrow and scaling up.
In this case it's 6.7 cm long which means the displacement is **6.7 m**.

To **subtract** vectors you need to **flip the direction** of the vector you are subtracting.
This **changes the sign** of the vector.
Adding the flipped vector is the **same** as **subtracting** the vector.
For example: 3 m – 4 m = 3 m + (– 4 m) = –1 m

...Or Use **Pythagoras** if the Vectors make a **Right Angle Triangle**

If two vectors, A and B, are at right angles to each other, you can also use Pythagoras' theorem to find the resultant. 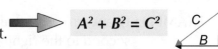 $A^2 + B^2 = C^2$

EXAMPLE: An object has an initial velocity of 3.0 ms^{-1} to the right, and a final velocity of 2.0 ms^{-1} down. Find the size of the change in velocity.

Change in velocity = Δv = final velocity – initial velocity.

First, flip the direction and change the sign of the vector that is being subtracted. 2.0 ms^{-1} – 3.0 ms^{-1} = 2.0 ms^{-1} + 3.0 ms^{-1} =

$A^2 + B^2 = C^2$, so $C = \sqrt{A^2+B^2} = \sqrt{2.0^2+3.0^2} = 3.605... = $ **3.6 ms^{-1} (to 2 s.f.)**

(This answer is rounded to 2 s.f. to match the data in the question — see page 1.)

Subtracting velocity vectors is easy — subtracting velociraptors, less so...

1) Find the size of the resultant of the following displacements by drawing the arrows "tip-to-tail".
   a) 5.0 m right and 4.0 m up.
   b) 15.0 miles south and 15.0 miles on a bearing of 045°.
2) Initial velocity = 1.0 ms^{-1} west and final velocity = 3.0 ms^{-1} north. Find the size of Δv.

Resolving Vectors

You can Split a *Vector* into *Horizontal* and *Vertical Components*

1) Vectors like **velocity** and **displacement** can be **split** into **components**.
2) This is basically the opposite of finding the resultant — you start from the resultant vector and split it into two separate vectors at **right angles** to each other.
3) Together these two components have the **same effect** as the **original** vector.
4) To find the components of a vector, v, you need to use **trigonometry**:

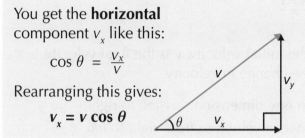

You get the **horizontal** component v_x like this:
$$\cos\theta = \frac{v_x}{v}$$
Rearranging this gives:
$$v_x = v\cos\theta$$

...and the **vertical** component v_y like this:
$$\sin\theta = \frac{v_y}{v}$$
Rearranging this gives:
$$v_y = v\sin\theta$$

You can also **rearrange** these equations to find θ. E.g. if you know v_x and v then:
$$\theta = \cos^{-1}\left(\frac{v_x}{v}\right)$$

Resolving is dead useful because the two components of a vector **don't affect each other**. This means you can deal with the two directions **completely separately**.

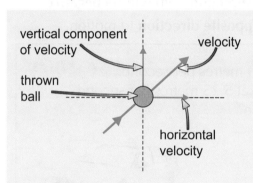

If you throw a ball diagonally up and to the right...
- Only the vertical component of the velocity is affected by gravity (see page 7).
- You can calculate the ball's vertical velocity (which will be affected by gravity).
- And you can calculate the ball's horizontal velocity (which won't be affected by gravity).

EXAMPLE: A helium balloon is floating away on the wind. It is travelling at 4.3 ms⁻¹ at an angle of 37° to the horizontal. What are the vertical and horizontal components of its velocity?

It's useful to start off by drawing a diagram:
Horizontal velocity = $v_x = v\cos\theta = 4.3 \times \cos 37$
$= 3.434... = $ **3.4 ms⁻¹ (to 2 s.f.)**
Vertical velocity = $v_y = v\sin\theta = 4.3 \times \sin 37$
$= 2.587... = $ **2.6 ms⁻¹ (to 2 s.f.)**

Solve these questions by re-solving the vectors...

1) A rugby ball is moving at 12 ms⁻¹ at an angle of 68° to the horizontal. Find the horizontal and vertical components of the ball's velocity.
2) A plane is travelling at 98 ms⁻¹ at a constant angle as it gains altitude. The horizontal velocity of the plane is 67 ms⁻¹. What is its angle of ascent?
3) A hot air balloon descends at a velocity of 5.9 ms⁻¹ at an angle of 23° to the horizontal. How long does it take the balloon to descend 150 m?

Acceleration

Acceleration — the Change in Velocity Every Second

Acceleration is the **rate of change** of **velocity**. Like velocity, it is a **vector quantity** (it has a size and a direction). It is measured in **metres per second squared** (ms⁻²).

$$\text{Acceleration (in metres per second}^2) = \frac{\text{change in velocity (in metres per second)}}{\text{time taken (in seconds)}}$$

So: $$\text{Acceleration} = \frac{\text{final velocity} - \text{initial velocity}}{\text{time taken}}$$

Or in symbols: $a = \dfrac{v-u}{t} = \dfrac{\Delta v}{t}$ where u is the initial velocity, v is the final velocity and Δv is the change in velocity.

You'll often only need to think about velocities in **one dimension**, say left to right.

But you still need to recognise the **difference** between velocities from right to left and velocities from left to right.

Choose a direction to be **positive** — below, we'll use **right**. All velocities in this direction will from now on be positive, and all those in the **opposite direction** (left) will be **negative**.

Deceleration is negative acceleration and acts in the **opposite direction** to motion.

EXAMPLE: A car starts off moving to the right at 15.0 metres per second. After 30.0 seconds it is moving to the left at 5.25 metres per second. What was its acceleration during this time?

u = 15.0 ms⁻¹ to the right = +15.0 ms⁻¹

v = 5.25 ms⁻¹ to the left = −5.25 ms⁻¹

So, $a = \dfrac{v-u}{t} = \dfrac{-5.25 - 15.0}{30.0} = \dfrac{-20.25}{30.0} = $ **−0.675 ms⁻²**

(The acceleration is negative so it's to the left.)

EXAMPLE: A dinosaur accelerates from rest at 4.00 ms⁻² to the right. If its final velocity is 25.0 ms⁻¹ to the right, how long does it accelerate for?

u = 0.00 ms⁻¹ v = 25.0 ms⁻¹ to the right = +25.0 ms⁻¹

$a = \dfrac{v-u}{t}$, multiplying both sides by t gives $a \times t = v - u$,

and then dividing both sides by a gives $t = \dfrac{v-u}{a}$. So, $t = \dfrac{25.0 - 0}{4.00} = $ **6.25 s**

A seller rating is the key thing to check when buying a car online...

1) A train has an initial velocity of 12.8 ms⁻¹ to the left. After 22.0 seconds it is moving to the right at 18.3 ms⁻¹. What was its average acceleration during this time?

2) A ship accelerates at a uniform rate of 0.18 ms⁻² east. If its initial velocity is 1.5 ms⁻¹ east and its final velocity is 4.5 ms⁻¹ in the same direction, how long has it been accelerating for?

3) A rabbit is hopping at a constant speed when he begins decelerating at a rate of 0.41 ms⁻². What was the rabbit's initial hopping speed if it takes him 3.7 seconds to come to a stop?

Acceleration Due To Gravity

The *Acceleration* Due to *Gravity* is *g*

When an object is dropped, it accelerates downwards at a constant rate of roughly
9.81 ms^{-2}. This is the **acceleration due to gravity** and it has the symbol *g*.

It usually seems sensible to take the upward direction as positive and down as negative,
making the acceleration due to gravity **–9.81 ms^{-2}**.

EXAMPLE: What is the vertical velocity of a skydiver 5.25 seconds
after she jumps out of a plane that is travelling at a constant
altitude? (Ignore air resistance and horizontal motion.)

$u = 0$

$a = -9.81$ ms^{-2}

You can rearrange $a = \frac{v-u}{t}$ to give $v = u + (a \times t)$.

So $v = 0 + (-9.81 \times 5.25)$

$\quad = 0 - 51.5025$

$\quad = -51.5025 = $ **51.5 ms^{-1} down (to 3 s.f.)**

EXAMPLE: A diver jumps up off a springboard. After 2.50 seconds he hits
the water travelling downwards at 18.0 ms^{-1}. What was his initial
vertical velocity? (Ignore air resistance and horizontal motion.)

$v = 18.0$ ms^{-1} down $= -18.0$ ms^{-1}

$a = -9.81$ ms^{-2}

You can rearrange $a = \frac{v-u}{t}$ to give $u = v - (a \times t)$.

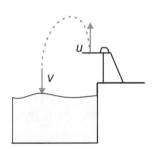

So, $u = -18.0 - (-9.81 \times 2.50)$

$\quad = -18.0 - (-24.525)$

$\quad = -18.0 + 24.525$

$\quad = 6.525 = $ **6.53 ms^{-1} upwards (to 3 s.f.)**

This isn't falling, it's learning with style...

You can ignore air resistance in these questions. Hint — drawing a little diagram can help.

1) An apple falls from a tree and hits the ground at 4.9 ms^{-1}. For how long was it falling?
2) A stone is thrown straight downwards. It hits the ground at 26.5 ms^{-1} after 2.15 seconds.
   What velocity was it thrown at?
3) A metal rod falls from a stationary helicopter.
   What velocity does it hit the ground at, 10.0 seconds later?
4) A sandbag is dropped from a stationary hot-air balloon. It hits the ground at a velocity
   of 24.5 metres per second. How long was it falling for?
5) A ball is thrown straight upwards. After 1.90 seconds it is moving downwards
   at 10.7 ms^{-1} and is caught. With what velocity was it thrown?

Displacement-Time Graphs

*You can **Draw Graphs** to Show **How Far** Something has **Travelled***

1) A graph of displacement against time tells you **how far** an object is from a given point, in a given direction, as time goes on.

2) As the object moves **away** from that point the **displacement** on the graph goes **up**, and as it moves **towards** it the displacement goes **down**:

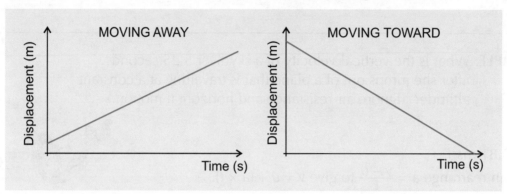

3) Important — these graphs only tell you about motion in **one dimension**. For example, a graph could tell you **how far up** a ball has been thrown, but **not** how far it has **moved horizontally**.

*The **Gradient** of the **Line** is the **Velocity***

Velocity = displacement ÷ time (see p.2), so the **gradient** (slope) of a displacement-time graph tells you **how fast** an object is travelling, and **what direction** it is moving in.
The **greater** the gradient, the **larger** the velocity.

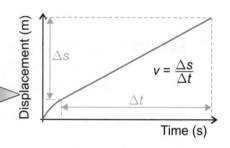

1) If the line is **straight**, the velocity is **constant**.

2) If the line is **curved**, the velocity is **changing** — the object is **accelerating** or decelerating.

3) A **steepening curve** means the **object is accelerating** and the **velocity** is getting **larger**.

4) A **flattening curve** means the **object is decelerating** and the **velocity** is getting **smaller**.

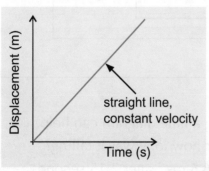
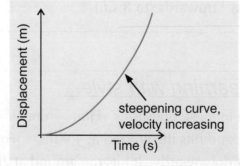
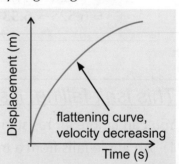

Steeper gradient = greater velocity — except when I try to run up a hill...

1) Sketch separate displacement-time graphs for a car in each of the following situations:
   a) Travelling away from the observer at a constant velocity.
   b) Travelling away from the observer and slowing down.
   c) Not moving, a short distance from the observer.
   d) Accelerating towards the observer.

Displacement-Time Graphs

EXAMPLE: The displacement-time graph below shows a motorcyclist accelerating to a constant speed, braking and then riding a short distance in the opposite direction.

You can read the following directly off the graph:

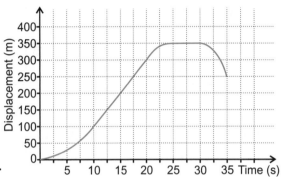

1) He took 10 s to accelerate to full speed and he travelled 100 m in that time.
2) He travelled at a constant velocity for the next 10 s and he travelled 200 m in that time.
3) He took 5 s to decelerate (by braking) and stop. He travelled 50 m in that time.
4) He remained stationary for 5 s at a displacement of 350 m from his starting point.
5) He accelerated in the opposite direction for 5 s.

You can work out three more details of the motorcyclist's journey:

1) The value of the **constant velocity** he travelled at between **10** and **20 seconds**.

velocity = gradient = $\dfrac{\text{change in displacement}}{\text{change in time}} = \dfrac{300-100}{20-10} = \dfrac{200}{10} = $ **20 ms⁻¹**

2) His **average velocity** for the **whole journey** — found by dividing his **overall change in displacement** by the **journey time**.

average velocity = $\dfrac{\text{final displacement} - \text{initial displacement}}{\text{total time taken}}$

$= \dfrac{250-0}{35} = \dfrac{250}{35} = 7.142... = $ **7.1 ms⁻¹ (to 2 s.f.)**

3) His **average speed** for the **whole journey** — found by dividing his **total distance travelled** by the **journey time**.
The total distance is the distance travelled in the positive direction (350 m) plus the distance travelled in the negative direction (100 m).

average speed = $\dfrac{\text{total distance travelled}}{\text{total time taken}} = \dfrac{350+100}{35} = = 12.85... = $ **13 ms⁻¹ (to 2 s.f.)**

Displacements — pretty lousy work experience if you ask me...

1) The displacement-time graph below shows the displacement of a racing car from the start line.

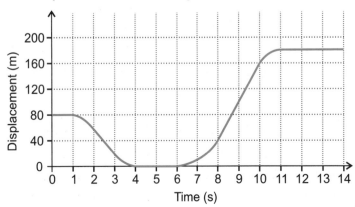

a) Is the car accelerating or decelerating between 1 s and 2 s?
b) Describe the motion of the car between 3 s and 6 s.
c) What is the velocity of the car between 8 s and 10 s?
d) What is the car's average velocity for the entire journey?
e) What is the car's average speed for the entire journey?

Velocity-Time Graphs

You can **Draw Graphs** to Show the **Velocity** of an **Object**

You can also draw graphs that show the **velocity** of an object moving in one dimension.

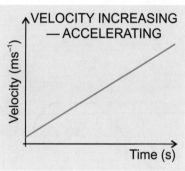
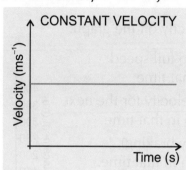
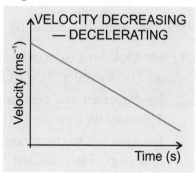

You can use a velocity-time graph to calculate two things:

1) The **distance** the object has moved.
2) The **acceleration**.

The **Area Under the Line** is the **Distance Travelled**

To find the **distance** an object **travels between two times**:

1) Draw **vertical lines** up from the horizontal axis at the two times.
2) Work out the **area** of the shape formed by these lines.
3) When you work out the area, you're **multiplying time** (the horizontal length) by **average speed** (the average vertical length), so the result is a **distance**.
4) You can work out the area in **two ways**:

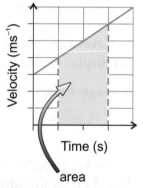

- Divide the shape into **trapeziums**, **triangles**, and/or **rectangles** and add up the **area** of each one.
- Or work out how many metres **each grid square** on the graph is worth, then **multiply by** the **number of squares under the line**. For squares cut by a **diagonal part** of the line, you'll need to **estimate** the **fraction** of the square that's under the line.

EXAMPLE: What is the distance travelled between 1 second and 5 seconds?

The shape made by the area between 1 and 5 seconds can be divided into a rectangle, a trapezium and a triangle.

So the total area = area of rectangle + area of trapezium + area of triangle.

Area of rectangle = width × height = 1 × 6 = 6 m

Area of trapezium = ½ × (left side + right side) × width
  = ½ × (6 + 4) × 2 = 5 × 2
  = 10 m

Area of triangle = ½ × width × height = ½ × 1 × 4 = 2 m

So distance travelled = 6 + 10 + 2 = **18 m**

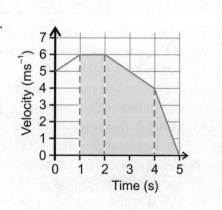

Velocity-Time Graphs

The *Gradient of the Line* is the *Acceleration*

The **acceleration** of an object travelling in **one dimension** (see page 6) is given by:

$$\text{Acceleration (in ms}^{-2}) = \frac{\text{change in velocity (in ms}^{-2})}{\text{time taken (in s)}}$$

This is just the **gradient** of a velocity-time graph. This means that a velocity-time graph of an object's motion has a **negative gradient** when an object is **slowing down** (decelerating).

EXAMPLE: What is the acceleration between 10 and 20 seconds?

Acceleration $= \dfrac{4-3}{20-10}$
$= \dfrac{1}{10}$
$= \textbf{0.1 ms}^{-2}$

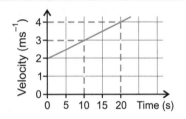

EXAMPLE: What is the acceleration between 5 and 15 seconds?

Acceleration $= \dfrac{10-15}{15-5}$
$= \dfrac{-5}{10}$
$= \textbf{−0.5 ms}^{-2}$

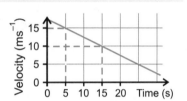

A *Curved Line* means the *Acceleration* is *Changing*

If the line is curved, the acceleration is **not constant**.
A **steepening** curve means the acceleration is **increasing**.
A **flattening** curve means the acceleration is **decreasing**.

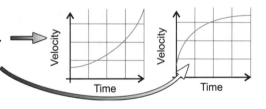

A steepening curve — my v-t graph when I find a spider in my room...

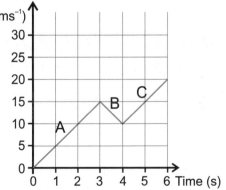

a) Calculate the acceleration shown in sections A, B and C on each graph.

b) Calculate the total distance travelled shown by each graph.

Adding and Resolving Forces

The **Resultant Force** is the **Sum** of **All** the **Forces**

1) Force is a **vector**, just like displacement or velocity.

2) When **more than one force** acts on a body, you can **add them together** in just the same way as you add displacements or velocities.

3) You find the **resultant force** by putting the arrows "tip-to-tail".

4) If the resultant force is **zero**, the forces are **balanced**.

5) If there's a resultant force, the forces are **unbalanced** and there's a **net force** on the object.

EXAMPLE: Find the resultant force on each object below and decide if the forces are balanced or unbalanced.

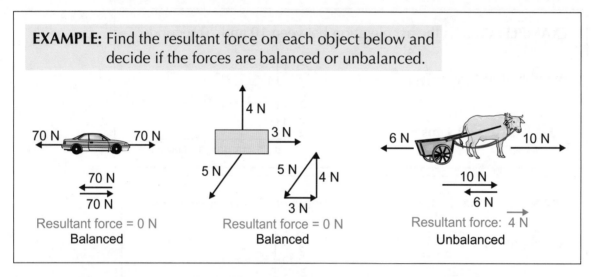

You can **Resolve Forces** just like **Other Vectors**

1) Forces can be in **any direction**, so they're not always at right angles to each other. This is sometimes a bit **awkward** for **calculations**.

2) To make an 'awkward' force easier to deal with, you can think of it as **two separate forces**, acting at **right angles** to **each other**. Forces are **vectors**, so you just use the method on p.5.

The force **F** has exactly the same effect as the horizontal and vertical forces, **F$_H$** and **F$_V$**. Use these formulas when resolving forces:

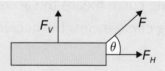

$$F_H = F\cos\theta \text{ and } F_V = F\sin\theta$$

Unbalanced forces — a police officer and a tank on a seesaw...

1) Work out the resultant forces on these objects. Are the forces are balanced or unbalanced?

a)

b)

c)

2) The engine of a plane provides a force of 920 N at an angle of 12° above the horizontal. What is the horizontal component of the force?

3) A kite surfer is pulled along a beach by a force of 150 N at an angle of 78° above the horizontal. What is the vertical component of the force?

Forces and Acceleration

Newton's *First Law* — a *Force* is Needed to *Change Velocity*

1) It's difficult to explain exactly what a "force" is, so instead we talk about what forces do.
2) Forces **stretch**, **squash** or **twist** things, but most importantly forces make things go **faster** (or **slower** or **change direction**).
3) **Newton's First Law** says that:

> The velocity of an object **will not change** unless a **resultant force** acts on it.

4) This means an object will **stay still** or **move** in a **straight line** at a **constant speed**, unless there's a **resultant force acting on it**.
5) A **resultant force** is when the forces acting on an object are **unbalanced** (see p.12) — e.g. when a car accelerates, the driving force from the engine is greater than the friction forces.
6) If there's a resultant force, the object will **accelerate** in the **direction** of the resultant force.

EXAMPLE: How does the velocity change in each of these examples?

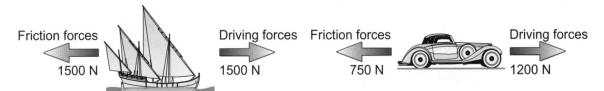

Friction forces 1500 N | Driving forces 1500 N
Resultant force = 1500 − 1500 = 0 N
No acceleration, so velocity doesn't change.

Friction forces 750 N | Driving forces 1200 N
Resultant force = 1200 − 750 = 450 N
Car accelerates, so velocity increases.

Friction forces 320 N | Driving forces 110 N
Resultant force = 110 − 320 = −210 N
Bike decelerates, so velocity decreases.

Newton's *Second Law* — *Acceleration* is *Proportional* to *Force*

1) According to Newton's First Law, applying a resultant force to an object makes it accelerate.
2) **Newton's Second Law** says that:

> The **acceleration** is **directly proportional** to the **resultant force**.

3) This means that if you **double** the **force applied** to an object, you **double its acceleration**.
4) You can write down this relationship as the equation:

resultant force (in newtons, N) = **mass** of object (in kg) × **acceleration** of object (in ms^{-2})

Or, in symbols:

$$F = m \times a$$

Forces and Acceleration

Here are some *Examples* of Newton's *Second Law*

EXAMPLE: A car of mass 1250 kg accelerates uniformly from rest to 15 ms⁻¹ in 25 s. What is the resultant force accelerating it?

$v = 15$ ms⁻¹, $u = 0$ ms⁻¹, $t = 25$ s

$a = \frac{v-u}{t}$, so $a = \frac{15-0}{25} = 0.60$ ms⁻²

Then $F = m \times a = 1250 \times 0.60 =$ **750 N**

EXAMPLE: A cyclist applies a braking force of 150 N to come to a stop from a speed of 2.5 ms⁻¹ in 2.3 s. What is the total mass of the cyclist and their bike?

$v = 0$ ms⁻¹, $u = 2.5$ ms⁻¹, $t = 2.3$ s

Again $a = \frac{v-u}{t} = \frac{0-2.5}{2.3} = -1.086...$ ms⁻²

The acceleration is negative because the cyclist is slowing down — the acceleration and the resultant force are in the opposite direction to the cyclist's motion.

Then $m = \frac{F}{a} = \frac{-150}{-1.086...} = 138 =$ **140 kg (to 2 s.f.)**

(This answer is rounded to 2 s.f. to match the data in the question — see page 1.)

Newton's *Third Law* — Forces have an *Equal, Opposite Reaction*

Newton's Third Law says that:

Each force has an **equal** and **opposite reaction** force.

This means that if object A exerts a force on object B, then object B must exert an **equal but opposite** force on object A.

For example — when you are **standing up**, you exert a force (your weight) on the floor and the floor **pushes back** with a force of the **same size** in the **opposite direction**. If it didn't you'd just **fall through the floor**...

Newton was awful at times tables — he was only interested in fours...

1) A car pulls a caravan of mass 840 kg. If the car accelerates at 0.50 ms⁻², what force will the caravan experience?

2) An apple of mass 0.120 kg falls with an acceleration of 9.81 ms⁻². What is the gravitational force pulling it down (its weight)?

3) An arrow of mass 0.5 kg is shot from a bow. If the force from the bow-string is 250 N, what is the initial acceleration of the arrow?

4) What is the mass of a ship if a force of 55 000 N produces an acceleration of 0.275 ms⁻²?

5) A train of mass 15 000 kg accelerates from rest for 25 s. If the total force from the engines is 8600 N, what is the train's final velocity?

SECTION 1 — FORCES AND MOTION

Kinetic Energy

Moving Things Have Kinetic Energy

Energy is a curious thing. You can't pick it up and look at it.

One thing's for certain though — if you're **moving** then you have energy.

This movement energy is more properly known as **kinetic energy**, and there's a formula for working it out:

> If a body of **mass** m (in kilograms) is moving with **speed** v (in metres per second) then its **kinetic energy** (in joules) is given by:
>
> **kinetic energy = ½ × mass × speed²**

Or, in symbols: $E_k = ½ × m × v^2$

Have a look at the following examples, and then try the questions after them.

EXAMPLE: A car of mass 1000 kg is travelling with a speed of 20 ms⁻¹. What is its kinetic energy?

$E_k = ½ × m × v^2$, so $E_k = ½ × 1000 × 20^2$
   $= ½ × 1000 × 400 = 200\,000 = \mathbf{2 × 10^5\ J}$

EXAMPLE: A ball has a speed of 2.5 ms⁻¹ and has kinetic energy equal to 0.75 J. What is the mass of the ball?

$E_k = ½ × m × v^2$

Multiplying both sides by 2 gives $2 × E_k = m × v^2$,

then dividing both sides by v^2 gives $\dfrac{2 × E_k}{v^2} = m$,

so $m = \dfrac{2 × E_k}{v^2} = \dfrac{2 × 0.75}{2.5 × 2.5} = \dfrac{1.5}{6.25} = \mathbf{0.24\ kg}$

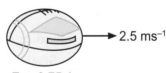

2.5 ms⁻¹

$E_k = 0.75$ J

EXAMPLE: A bullet has kinetic energy equal to 1200 J. If its mass is 15 g, what is its speed?

$m = 15$ g $= 0.015$ kg

From the previous example: $2 × E_k = m × v^2$

Dividing both sides by m gives $\dfrac{2 × E_k}{m} = v^2$,

then taking square roots of both sides gives $\sqrt{\dfrac{2 × E_k}{m}} = v$,

so $v = \sqrt{\dfrac{2 × E_k}{m}} = \sqrt{\dfrac{2 × 1200}{0.015}} = \mathbf{400\ ms^{-1}}$

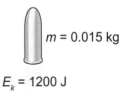

$m = 0.015$ kg

$E_k = 1200$ J

Kinetic energy — what you need lots of when you're late for the bus...

1) An arrow of mass 0.125 kg is travelling at a speed of 72.0 ms⁻¹. What is its kinetic energy?

2) A ship has kinetic energy equal to $5.4 × 10^7$ J when moving at 15 ms⁻¹. What is its mass?

3) A snail of mass 57 g has a kinetic energy of $1.0 × 10^{-6}$ J. What is its speed?

Gravitational Potential Energy

Gravitational Potential Energy Depends on Height and Mass

When an object **falls**, its speed **increases**. As its speed increases, so does its **kinetic energy**.
Where does it get this energy from?

Answer — from the **gravitational potential energy** it had before it fell:

> If a body of **mass m** (in kilograms) is **raised** through a **height h** (in metres),
> the **gravitational potential energy** (in joules) it gains is given by:
> **gravitational potential energy = mass × gravitational field strength × height**

So, in symbols it reads:

$$E_p = m \times g \times h$$

The gravitational field strength, g, is the **ratio** of an object's
weight to its **mass** (in newtons per kilogram, Nkg^{-1}).

At the surface of the Earth, g has an approximate value of **$9.81\ Nkg^{-1}$**.

EXAMPLE: An 80.0 kilogram person in a lift is raised 45.0 metres.
What is the increase in the person's gravitational potential energy?

$E_p = m \times g \times h$, so $E_p = 80.0 \times 9.81 \times 45.0 = 35\ 316 =$ **35 300 J (to 3 s.f.)**

EXAMPLE: A mass raised 15.0 metres gains gravitational potential energy
equal to 50.0 joules. What is that mass?

$E_p = m \times g \times h$. Dividing both sides by g and h gives $\dfrac{E_p}{g \times h} = m$,

so $m = \dfrac{E_p}{g \times h} = \dfrac{50.0}{9.81 \times 15.0} = 0.3397... =$ **0.340 kg (to 3 s.f.)**

$E_p = 50.0\ J$

$h = 15.0\ m$

EXAMPLE: 725 kilograms of bricks are given 29 400 joules of gravitational
potential energy. Through what height have they been raised?

$E_p = m \times g \times h$. Dividing both sides by m and g gives $\dfrac{E_p}{m \times g} = h$,

so $h = \dfrac{E_p}{m \times g} = \dfrac{29\ 400}{725 \times 9.81} = 4.1337... =$ **4.13 m (to 3 s.f.)**

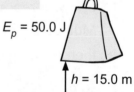

$E_p = 29\ 400\ J$

$m = 725\ kg$

Liven up your roasts — pour on some graveytational potential energy...

1) How much more gravitational potential energy does a 750 kg car
   have at the top of a 350 m high hill than at the bottom?

2) A crate is raised through 7.00 metres and gains 1715 J of gravitational
   potential energy. What is the mass of the crate?

3) A 65.0 kilogram hiker gains 24 700 joules of gravitational potential energy
   when climbing a small hill. How high have they climbed?

Conservation of Energy

The *Conservation of Energy* Applies to *Falling Bodies*

The principle of **conservation of energy** states that:

"Energy **cannot** be **created** or **destroyed** — it can only be **converted** into other forms"

So as long as you ignore air resistance...

...for a **falling** object:

kinetic energy gained (in joules) = **gravitational potential energy lost** (in joules)

...and for an object **thrown** or **catapulted** upwards:

gravitational potential energy gained (in joules) = **kinetic energy lost** (in joules)

This can be very useful in solving problems.
Read through the examples and then have a go at the questions afterwards.
(In all the questions, you can ignore air resistance.)

EXAMPLE: An apple of mass 0.165 kilograms falls 2.00 metres from a tree.
What speed does it hit the ground at?

E_p lost $= m \times g \times h = 0.165 \times 9.81 \times 2.00 = 3.2373$ J

Therefore E_k gained $= 3.2373$ J. $E_k = \frac{1}{2} \times m \times v^2$.

Rearranging this gives $v = \sqrt{\dfrac{2 \times E_k}{m}}$, so $v = \sqrt{\dfrac{2 \times 3.2373}{0.165}} = 6.264...$

$= \textbf{6.26 ms}^{-1}$ **(to 3 s.f.)**

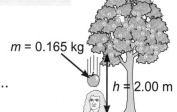

$m = 0.165$ kg

$h = 2.00$ m

EXAMPLE: A model clown of mass 225 grams is fired straight upwards from
a cannon at 10.0 metres per second. How high does it get?

$m = 225$ g $= 0.225$ kg

E_k lost $= \frac{1}{2} \times m \times v^2 = \frac{1}{2} \times 0.225 \times 10.0^2 = 11.25$ J

Therefore, E_p gained $= 11.25$ J. $E_p = m \times g \times h$.

Rearranging this gives $h = \dfrac{E_p}{m \times g}$, so $h = \dfrac{11.25}{0.225 \times 9.81}$

$= 5.096... = \textbf{5.10 m}$ **(to 3 s.f.)**

$h = ?$

$m = 0.225$ kg
$v = 10.0$ ms^{-1}

Today I'm practising conservation of energy — I'm staying in bed all day...

1) A gymnast jumps vertically upwards from a trampoline with 2850 J of kinetic energy.
   They climb to a height of 5.10 m. What is the gymnast's mass?

2) A book of mass 0.475 kilograms falls off a table top 92.0 centimetres from the floor.
   What speed is it travelling at when it hits the floor?

3) A bullet of mass 0.015 kilograms is fired upwards at 420 ms^{-1}. What height does it reach?

Work

Work — the Amount of Energy Transferred by a Force

When you **move** an object by **applying a force** to it, you are **doing work** (generally against another force) and **transferring energy**. For example:

1) **Lifting** up a box — you are doing work against gravity.
   The energy is transferred to gravitational potential energy.

2) **Pushing** a wheely chair across a room — you are doing work against friction.
   The energy is transferred to heat and kinetic energy.

3) **Stretching** a spring — you are doing work against the stiffness of the spring.
   The energy is transferred to elastic potential energy stored in the spring.

The amount of energy (in joules) that a force transfers is called the **work done**. It's given by:

| **work done** by a force (in joules) | = | **size of force** (in newtons) | × | **distance the object moves** in the direction of the force while the force is acting (in metres) |

Or, in symbols: $W = F \times s$

> **EXAMPLE:** A 5.0 newton force pushes a box 3.0 metres in the same direction as the force. What is the work done by the force?
>
> $W = F \times s$, so $W = 5.0 \times 3.0 = $ **15 J**

The Force isn't Always in the Same Direction as the Movement

Sometimes the force acts in a **different direction** to the object's movement.

For example — when you **pull** on a sledge, the force acts **diagonally** along the rope but the sledge only moves **horizontally**.

So it's only the **horizontal part** of the force that is doing any work.

You need to use some **trigonometry** to find the work done:

$W = F \cos \theta \times s$ (See page 12 for more about resolving forces.)

direction of motion

direction of force, F, on sledge

angle, θ

horizontal force = $F\cos\theta$

> **EXAMPLE:** A 25 newton force to the north-east pushes an object 15 metres in a northerly direction. What is the work done?
>
> Use trigonometry to find the part of the force that acts in the direction of travel (i.e. north).
>
> North-east = 045°, so $F\cos\theta = 25 \times \cos45° = 17.677...$ N
>
> So the work done is $W = F\cos\theta \times s = 17.677... \times 15 = 265.165... = $ **270 J (to 2 s.f.)**

N   NE

45°   25 N

Work is F times s, what a way to make a living...

1) An upwards force of 25 newtons lifts an object 44 metres. What is the work done?

2) A boy pulls a toy cart 2.5 m along the ground. He applies a force of 17 N at an angle of 35° to the horizontal. How much work does he do?

Work

Work Done = *Increase* in *Gravitational* and *Kinetic Energy*

If a force does work on an object, a few things can happen. For example:

The **work done** can go **entirely** into the **gravitational potential energy** of the object:

EXAMPLE: A force does 74 J of work lifting a 3.0 kg cheese straight up. How high is the cheese lifted?

Work done = increase in gravitational potential energy, so:

$W = m \times g \times h$, and so $h = \frac{W}{m \times g}$

$h = \frac{74}{3.0 \times 9.81} = 2.514... = $ **2.5 m (to 2 s.f.)**

$W = m \times g \times h$

The **work done** can go **entirely** into the **kinetic energy** of the object:

EXAMPLE: The same cheese (of mass 3.0 kg) is pushed horizontally along a frictionless surface with a force of 5.7 N over a distance of 12 m. What is its final speed, assuming it was initially at rest?

Work done = increase in kinetic energy, so:

$W = F \times s = \frac{1}{2} \times m \times v^2$, so $v = \sqrt{2 \times \frac{F \times s}{m}}$

$v = \sqrt{2 \times \frac{5.7 \times 12}{3.0}} = 6.752... = $ **6.8 ms⁻¹ (to 2 s.f.)**

$F = 5.7$ N
$m = 3.0$ kg
$s = 12$ m

The **work done** can go into increasing **both** the **kinetic** and the **gravitational energy**:

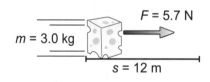

EXAMPLE: The same cheese is fired diagonally upwards from a catapult. At its highest point it has climbed 19 m and is moving horizontally at 12 ms⁻¹. How much work was done on the cheese?

Work done = increase in E_k + increase in E_p, so:

$F \times s = (\frac{1}{2} \times m \times v^2) + (m \times g \times h)$
$\quad = (\frac{1}{2} \times 3.0 \times 12^2) + (3.0 \times 9.81 \times 19.0)$
$\quad = 775.17 = $ **780 J (to 2 s.f.)**

$v = 12$ ms⁻¹
$h = 19$ m

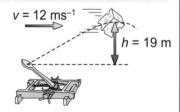

Work done? No, you need to answer this question first...

1) A constant 125 N force lifts a 5.75 kg rocket vertically upwards. When the rocket reaches a height of 2.50 m the force is removed, but the rocket continues to move upwards. Calculate:
   a) the work done by the force.
   b) the gain in gravitational potential energy.
   c) the gain in kinetic energy.
   d) the upwards speed of the rocket immediately after the force is removed.

Power

Power — the Work Done *Every Second*

In mechanical situations, **whenever** energy is **converted**, **work** is being done.

For example, when an object is **falling**, the force of **gravity** is doing work on that object **equal** to the **increase** in **kinetic energy** (ignoring air resistance).

The **rate** at which this work is being done is called the **power**.

You can calculate it using:

> **power** (in watts) = **work done** (in joules) ÷ **time taken** (in seconds)

Or, in symbols: $P = \dfrac{W}{t}$

Power is measured in **watts**.

A watt is equivalent to **one joule of work done per second**.

EXAMPLE: If 10 joules of work are done in 2 seconds, what is the power?

$P = W \div t = 10 \div 2 = \textbf{5 W}$

EXAMPLE: For how long must a 3.2 kilowatt (3.2×10^3 watt) engine run to do 480 kilojoules (4.8×10^5 joules) of work?

$P = W \div t$

Multiplying both sides by t gives: $P \times t = W$

Then dividing both sides by P gives: $t = W \div P$

So, $t = W \div P = \dfrac{4.8 \times 10^5}{3.2 \times 10^3} = \textbf{150 s}$

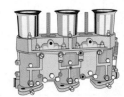

EXAMPLE: A force of 125 newtons pushes a crate 5.2 metres in 2.6 seconds. What is the power? (The motion is in the same direction as the force.)

First you need to find the work done (see page 18):

$W = F \times s = 125 \times 5.2 = 650 \text{ J}$

Then use W to find the power:

$P = W \div t = 650 \div 2.6 = \textbf{250 W}$

The power of love ain't that special — it's just a lot of work over time...

1) What is the power output of a motor if it does 250 joules of work in 4.0 seconds?
2) If a lift mechanism works at 14 kilowatts, how long does it take to do 91 kilojoules of work?
3) An engine provides a force of 276 N to push an object 1.25 km in 2.5 minutes. What power is the engine working at?

Power

Power is also Force Multiplied By Speed

There's a **useful equation** you can **derive** for the **work done** by a force **every second** on an object moving at a **constant speed**. Follow through the working in the example below:

> **EXAMPLE:** What power is a car engine working at if it produces a driving force of 2100 newtons when moving at a steady speed of 32 metres per second?
>
>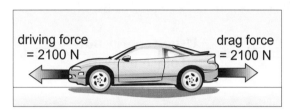
>
> driving force = 2100 N   drag force = 2100 N
>
> The car is moving at a steady speed. This means the forces on it are balanced, so the driving force must be equal to the drag force.
>
> The power of the engine is given by $P = W \div t$.
>
> $W = F \times s$, so we can substitute for the work done, giving $P = \frac{F \times s}{t}$.
>
> Now, $\frac{F \times s}{t}$ is the same as $F \times \frac{s}{t}$, so $P = F \times \frac{s}{t}$.
>
> Finally we use the fact that $\frac{s}{t} = \dfrac{\text{distance travelled}}{\text{time taken}} =$ the speed, v.
>
> $$\text{So,} \quad P = F \times \tfrac{s}{t} = F \times v$$
>
> **power** (in watts) = **force** (in newtons) × **speed** (in metres per second)
>
> For our example, $P = 2100 \times 32 = 67\,200 = \textbf{67\,000 W}$ (or 67 kW) **(to 2 s.f.)**
>
> (This answer is rounded to 2 s.f. to match the data in the question — see page 1.)

IMPORTANT:
The formula $P = F \times v$ is **only** true when the object is moving at a **constant speed** in the **same direction as the force**.

Moooving forces with a lot of power — a stampeding herd of cows...

1) What is the power delivered by a train engine if its driving force of 1.80×10^5 newtons produces a constant speed of 40.0 metres per second?

2) A skydiver is falling at a constant velocity of 45 metres per second. Gravity is doing work on her at a rate of 31 500 joules per second. What is her weight?

3) A car is travelling at steady speed. Its engine delivers a power of 5.20×10^4 watts to provide a force of 1650 newtons. What speed is the car travelling at (in metres per second)?

Efficiency

How Much of What You **Put In** Do You **Get Out**?

1) For most mechanical systems you **put in** energy in **one form** and the system **gives out** energy in **another**.

2) However, **some** energy is **always** converted into forms that **aren't useful**.

3) For example, an electric motor converts electrical energy into **heat** and **sound** as well as useful kinetic energy.

4) You can measure the **efficiency** of a system by the **percentage of total energy put in that is converted to useful forms**.

$$\text{Efficiency} = \frac{\text{Useful energy out}}{\text{Total energy in}} \times 100\%$$

EXAMPLE: A pirate uses a rope to pull a box of mass 4.5 kg vertically upwards through 5.0 m of water. He pulls with a force of 98 N. What is the efficiency of this system?

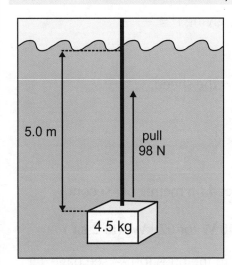

The **energy the pirate puts in** is the work he does pulling the rope.

The **useful energy out** is the gravitational potential energy gained by the box.

Some energy is converted to heat and sound by **friction** as the box is dragged through the water.

Total energy in = work done = $F \times s$
$= 98 \times 5.0$
$= 490$ J

Useful energy out = gravitational potential energy gained
$= m \times g \times h$
$= 4.5 \times 9.81 \times 5.0$
$= 220.725$ J

So, efficiency $= \dfrac{\text{Useful energy out}}{\text{Total energy in}} \times 100\%$

$= \dfrac{220.725}{490} \times 100\% = 45.045... = \mathbf{45\%}$ **(to 2 s.f.)**

Efficiency – getting on with these questions instead of messing about...

1) A motor uses 375 joules of electrical energy in lifting a 12.9 kilogram mass through 2.50 metres. What is its efficiency?

2) It takes 1.4 megajoules (1.4×10^6 joules) of chemical energy from the petrol in a car engine to accelerate a 560 kilogram car from rest to 25 metres per second on a flat road.
   a) What is the gain in kinetic energy?
   b) What is the efficiency of the car?

Forces and Springs

Hooke's Law — Extension is Directly Proportional to Force

1) When you apply a **force** to an object you can cause it to **stretch** and **deform** (change shape).

2) **Elastic objects** are objects that return to their **original shape** after this deforming force is **removed**, e.g. springs.

3) When a **spring** is supported at the top and a **weight** is attached to the bottom, it **stretches**.

4) The **extension**, Δl, of a spring is **directly proportional** to the **force** applied, F. This is **Hooke's Law**.

5) This relationship is also true for many other elastic objects like **metal wires**.

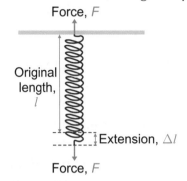

force	=	spring constant	×	extension
(in newtons, N)		(in newtons per metre, Nm⁻¹)		(in metres, m)

$$F = k \times \Delta l$$

The **spring constant**, k, depends on the stiffness of the **material** that you are stretching. It's measured in **newtons per metre** (Nm^{-1}).

EXAMPLE: A force is applied to a spring with a spring constant of 65.0 Nm⁻¹. The spring extends by 12.3 cm. What size is the force?

$F = k \times \Delta l$
$\Delta l = 12.3$ cm $= 0.123$ m
So, $F = 65.0 \times 0.123$
    $= 7.995$
    $= \textbf{8.00 N (to 3 s.f.)}$

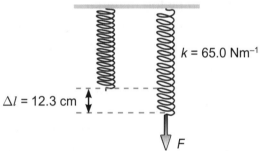

EXAMPLE: A sack of flour of mass 7.10 kg is attached to the bottom of a vertical spring. The spring constant is 85.0 Nm⁻¹ and the top of the spring is supported. How much does the spring extend by?

$F = k \times \Delta l$, so $\Delta l = \dfrac{F}{k}$
You need to work out the force from the given mass:
$F = $ weight of flour $= m \times g$
  $= 7.10 \times 9.81 = 69.651$ N
So, $\Delta l = \dfrac{69.651}{85.0}$
    $= 0.8194...$
    $= \textbf{0.819 m (to 3 s.f.)}$

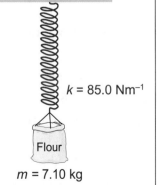

Forces and Springs

Hooke's Law **Stops Working** when the **Force** is **Great Enough**

There's a **limit** to the amount of force you can apply to an object for the extension to keep on increasing **proportionally**.

1) The graph shows **force** against **extension** for a spring.

2) For **small** forces, force and extension are **proportional**. So the first part of the graph shows a **straight-line relationship** between force and extension.

3) There is a **maximum force** that the spring can take and **still extend proportionally**. This is known as the **limit of proportionality** and is shown on the graph at the point marked **P**.

4) The point marked **E** is the **elastic limit**. If you increase the force past this point, the spring will be **permanently stretched**. When the force is **removed**, the spring will be **longer** than at the start.

5) Beyond the **elastic limit**, we say that the spring deforms **plastically**.

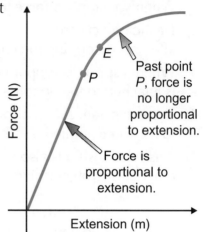

Past point P, force is no longer proportional to extension.

Force is proportional to extension.

Work Done can be **Stored** as **Elastic Strain Energy**

1) When a material is **stretched**, **work** has to be done in stretching the material.

2) If a deformation is **elastic**, all the work done is **stored** as **elastic strain energy** (also called **elastic potential energy**) in the material.

3) When the stretching force is removed, this **stored energy** is **transferred** to **other forms** — e.g. when an elastic band is stretched and then fired across a room, elastic strain energy is transferred to kinetic energy.

4) If a deformation is **plastic**, work is done to **separate atoms**, and energy is **not** stored as strain energy (it's mostly lost as heat).

Spring into action — force yourself to learn all this...

1) A force applied to a spring with spring constant 64.1 Nm⁻¹ causes it to extend by 24.5 cm. What was the force applied to the spring?

2) A pile of bricks is hung off a spring with spring constant 84.0 Nm⁻¹. The bricks apply a force of 378 N on the spring. How much does the spring extend by?

3) The mass limit for each bag taken on a flight with Cheapskate Airways is 9.0 kg. The mass of each bag is measured by attaching the bag to a spring.

   a) A bag of mass 7.4 kg extends the spring by 8.4 cm. What is the spring constant?

   b) The first bag is removed and another bag is attached to the spring. The spring extends by 9.5 cm. Can this bag be taken on the flight?

4) a) What is meant by the limit of proportionality?

   b) Why might a spring not return to its original length after having been stretched and then released?

Current and Potential Difference

Electric Current — *the Rate of Flow of Charge Around a Circuit*

1) In a circuit, **negatively-charged electrons** flow from the **negative** end of a battery to the **positive** end.

2) This flow of charge is called an **electric current**.

3) However, you can also think of current as a flow of **positive charge** in the **other direction**, from **positive** to **negative**. This is called **conventional current**.

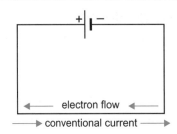

The electric current at a point in the wire is defined as:

$$\text{current (in amperes, A)} = \frac{\text{the } \textbf{amount of charge} \text{ passing the point (in coulombs, C)}}{\text{the } \textbf{time it takes} \text{ for the charge to pass (in seconds, s)}}$$

Or, in symbols: $I = \dfrac{Q}{t}$

EXAMPLE: 585 C of charge passes a point in a circuit in 45.0 s. What is the current at this point?

$I = \dfrac{Q}{t}$, so $I = \dfrac{585}{45.0} = \textbf{13.0 A}$

Potential Difference (Voltage) — *the Energy Per Unit Charge*

1) In all circuits, energy is **transferred** from the power supply to the **components**.

2) The **power supply** does **work** on the **charged particles**, which **carry** this energy **around** the circuit.

3) The potential difference **across a component** is defined as the **work done** (or energy transferred) **per coulomb** of charge moved through the component.

$$\textbf{Potential difference across component} \text{ (in volts, V)} = \frac{\textbf{work done} \text{ (in joules, J)}}{\textbf{charge moved} \text{ (in coulombs, C)}}$$

In symbols: $V = \dfrac{W}{Q}$

EXAMPLE: A component does 10.8 J of work for every 2.70 C that passes through it. What is the potential difference across the component?

$V = \dfrac{W}{Q}$, so $V = \dfrac{10.8}{2.70} = \textbf{4.00 V}$

Physicists love camping trips — they get to study po-tent-ial difference...

1) How long does it take to transfer 12 C of charge if the average current is 3.0 A?

2) The potential difference across a bulb is 1.5 V.
How much work is done to pass 9.2 C through the bulb?

3) A motor runs for 275 seconds and does 9540 J of work.
If the current in the circuit is 3.80 A, what is the potential difference across the motor?

Current in Electric Circuits

Charge is *Always Conserved* in Circuits

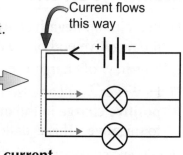

Current flows this way

1) As **charge flows** through a circuit, it **doesn't** get **used up** or **lost**.

2) You can easily build a circuit in which the electric current can be **split** between **two wires** — two lamps connected in **parallel** is a good example.

3) Because charge is **conserved** in circuits, whatever charge flows **into** a junction will flow **out** again.

4) Since **current** is **rate of flow of charge**, it follows that whatever **current flows into** a junction is the **same** as the **current flowing out** of it.

> the **sum** of the **currents going into the junction** = the **sum** of the **currents going out**

This is **Kirchhoff's first law**. It means that the current is the **same** everywhere in a **series circuit**, and is **shared between the branches** of a **parallel circuit**.

5) N.B. — current arrows on circuit diagrams normally show the direction of flow of **conventional current** (see p.25).

EXAMPLE: Use Kirchoff's first law to find the unknown current I_1.

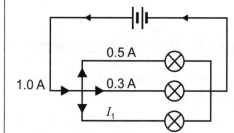

0.5 A

1.0 A   0.3 A

I_1

Sum of currents in = sum of currents out

$1.0 = 0.5 + 0.3 + I_1$

$1.0 = 0.8 + I_1$

$I_1 = 1.0 - 0.8$

$I_1 = \mathbf{0.2\ A}$

EXAMPLE: Calculate the missing currents, I_1 and I_2, in this circuit.

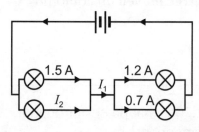

1.5 A   1.2 A

I_2 I_1 0.7 A

Looking at the junction immediately after I_1:

$I_1 = 1.2 + 0.7$

$I_1 = \mathbf{1.9\ A}$

And looking at the junction immediately before I_1:

$1.5 + I_2 = 1.9$

$I_2 = 1.9 - 1.5$

$I_2 = \mathbf{0.4\ A}$

Conserve charge — make nature reserves for circuit boards...

1) What is the value of I_1?

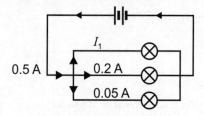

I_1

0.5 A   0.2 A

0.05 A

2) What is the value of I_2?

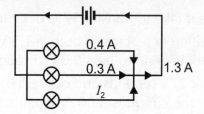

0.4 A

0.3 A   1.3 A

I_2

Potential Difference in Electric Circuits

Energy is *Always Conserved* in *Circuits*

1) Energy is **given** to **charged particles** by the **power supply** and **taken off them** by the **components** in the circuit.

2) Since energy is **conserved**, the **amount** of energy one coulomb of charge loses when going around the circuit must be **equal to** the energy it's **given** by the power supply.

3) This must be true **regardless** of the **route** the charge takes around the circuit. This means that:

> For any **closed loop** in a circuit, the **sum** of the **potential differences** across the components **equals** the **potential difference** of the **power supply**.

This **Kirchhoff's second law.** It means that:

- In a **series circuit**, the potential difference of the power supply is split between all the components.

- In a **parallel circuit**, each **loop** has the same potential difference as the power supply.

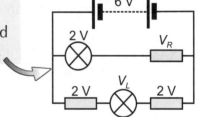

EXAMPLE: Use Kirchoff's second law to calculate the potential differences across the resistor, V_R, and the lamp, V_L, in the circuit shown on the right.

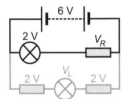

First look at just the top loop:

p.d. of power supply = sum of p.d.s of components in top loop

$6 = 2 + V_R$

So $V_R = 6 - 2 = $ **4 V**

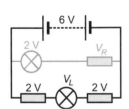

Now look at just the outside loop:

p.d. of power supply = sum of p.d.s of components in outside loop

$6 = 2 + V_L + 2$

So $V_L = 6 - 2 - 2 = $ **2 V**

This page is potentially tricky — so have a read of it all again...

1) For the circuit on the right, calculate:
   a) the voltage across the motor, V_M.
   b) the voltage across the loudspeaker, V_S.

2) A third loop containing two filament lamps is added to the circuit in parallel with the first two loops. What is the sum of the voltages of the two filament lamps?

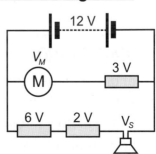

Resistance

Resistance — The Ratio of Potential Difference to Current

1) If there's a potential difference **across** a component a **current** will **flow through it**.

2) Usually, as the **potential difference** is **increased** the **current increases** — this makes sense if you think of the potential difference as a kind of force **pushing** the charged particles.

3) You can link current and potential difference by defining "**resistance**":

$$\text{Resistance of component (in ohms, } \Omega) = \frac{\text{potential difference across component (in volts, V)}}{\text{current passing through component (in amps, A)}}$$

Or, in symbols: $\quad R = \dfrac{V}{I}$

Multiplying both sides by I gives: $\quad V = I \times R$

4) Components with a **low resistance** allow a **large** current to flow through them, while components with a **high resistance** allow only a **small** current.

5) The resistance **isn't** always **constant** though — it can take **different values** as the **current** and **voltage change**, or it can change with conditions like **temperature** and **light level**.

EXAMPLE: If a potential difference of 12 V across a component causes a current of 1.0 mA to flow through it, what is the resistance of the component?

$R = \dfrac{V}{I}$, so $R = \dfrac{12}{1.0 \times 10^{-3}} = $ **12 000 Ω**, or 12 kΩ

EXAMPLE: What potential difference must be applied across a lamp with a resistance of 200 Ω in order for a current of 0.2 A to flow through it?

$V = I \times R$, so $V = 0.2 \times 200 = $ **40 V**

EXAMPLE: What current will flow through an 850 Ω resistor if a potential difference of 6.3 V is applied across it?

$V = I \times R$. Dividing both sides by R gives $I = \dfrac{V}{R}$,

so $I = \dfrac{6.3}{850} = 0.007411... = $ **0.0074 A** (or 7.4 mA) **(to 2 s.f.)**

Ohm my, look at that — more questions to do...

1) If a current of 2.5 amps flows through a component with a resistance of 15 ohms, what is the potential difference across the component?

2) What current will flow through a 2500 Ω resistor if the voltage across it is 6.0 volts?

3) What is the resistance of a component if 1.5 volts drives a current of 0.024 amps through it?

I-V Graphs

Ohm's Law Says Potential Difference is Proportional to Current

1) An *I-V* graph is a graph of **current** against **potential difference** for a component. For any *I-V* graph, the **resistance** at a given point is the potential difference divided by the current ($R = \frac{V}{I}$).

2) Provided the **temperature** is **constant**, the **current** through an **ohmic component** (e.g. a resistor) is **directly proportional** to the **potential difference** across it ($V \propto I$). This is called **Ohm's Law**.

3) An **ohmic component's** *I-V* graph is a **straight line**, with a gradient equal to 1 ÷ the resistance of the component. The **resistance** (and therefore the **gradient**) is **constant**.

- So for an ohmic component, **doubling** the **potential difference doubles** the **current**.
- Often **external factors**, such as **temperature**, will have a **significant effect** on resistance, so you need to remember that Ohm's law is **only** true for components like resistors at **constant temperature**.

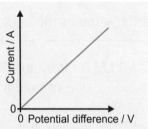

4) Sometimes you'll see a graph with **negative** values for p.d. and current. This just means the current is flowing the **other way** (so the terminals of the power supply have been switched).

EXAMPLE: Look at the *I-V* graph for a resistor on the right. What is its resistance when the potential difference across it is: a) 10 V, b) 5 V, c) –5 V, d) –10 V?

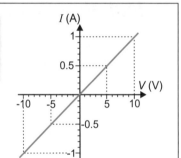

a) $R = \frac{V}{I} = \frac{10}{1} = 10\ \Omega$ b) $R = \frac{V}{I} = \frac{5}{0.5} = 10\ \Omega$

c) $R = \frac{V}{I} = \frac{-5}{-0.5} = 10\ \Omega$ d) $R = \frac{V}{I} = \frac{-10}{-1} = 10\ \Omega$

I-V Graphs for Other Components Aren't Straight Lines

The *I-V* graphs for **other** components **don't** have **constant gradients**. This means the resistance **changes** with voltage.

1) As the p.d. across a filament lamp gets **larger**, the filament gets **hotter** and its resistance **increases**.

2) Diodes only let current flow in **one direction**. The resistance of a diode is **very high** in the **other** direction.

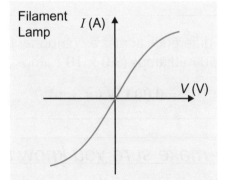
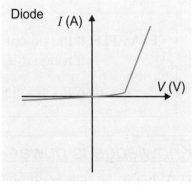

I-Ve decided you need amp-le practice to keep your knowledge current...

1) State Ohm's law.
2) Sketch *I-V* graphs for: a) an ohmic resistor, b) a filament lamp, c) a diode.

Power in Circuits

Power — the Rate of Transfer of Energy

1) Components in electrical circuits transfer the **energy** carried by electrons into other forms.
2) The **work done each second** (or the **energy transferred each second**)
   is the **power** of a component:

$$\textbf{power (in watts, W)} = \frac{\textbf{work done (in joules, J)}}{\textbf{time taken (in seconds, s)}}$$

Or, in symbols: $P = \dfrac{W}{t}$

This is the same as the equation for mechanical power that you saw on page 20.

EXAMPLE: A lift motor does 3.0×10^5 J of work in a single one-minute journey. At what power is it working?

$P = \dfrac{W}{t}$, so $P = \dfrac{3.0 \times 10^5}{60} = $ **5000 W** (or 5 kW)

Calculating Power from Current and Potential Difference

The work done is equal to the potential difference across the component multiplied by the amount of charge that has flowed through it ($W = V \times Q$) — see p.25.

So: $P = \dfrac{V \times Q}{t}$

The amount of charge that flows through a component is equal to the current through it multiplied by the time taken ($Q = I \times t$) — see p.25 again.

So: $P = \dfrac{V \times I \times t}{t}$

Cancelling the t's gives: $P = V \times I$

power (in watts) = **potential difference** (in volts) × **current** (in amps)

EXAMPLE: If the potential difference across a component is 6 volts and the current through it is 0.50 milliamps (5.0×10^{-4} amps), at what rate is it doing work?

$P = V \times I$, so $P = 6 \times 5.0 \times 10^{-4} = $ **0.003 W** (or 3 mW)

Knowledge is power — make sure you know these power equations...

1) What is the power output of a component if the current through it is 0.12 amps when the potential difference across it is 6.5 volts?
2) An electric heater has an operating power of 45 W.
   a) What current passes through the heater when the potential difference across it is 14 volts?
   b) How much work does the heater do in 12 seconds?

Power in Circuits

You Can **Combine** the Equations for **Power** and **Resistance**

You can **combine** the last equation for the power of an electrical component, $P = V \times I$, with the **equation** for resistance, $R = \frac{V}{I}$ (see p.28), to create two **more useful** equations.

1) Substitute $V = I \times R$ into $P = V \times I$ to get: $P = I \times R \times I = I^2R$

power (in watts) = [**current** (in amps)]^2 × **resistance** (in ohms)

2) Or substitute $I = \frac{V}{R}$ into $P = V \times I$ to get: $P = V \times \frac{V}{R} = \frac{V^2}{R}$

power (in watts) = $\frac{[\textbf{potential difference} \text{ (in volts)}]^2}{\textbf{resistance} \text{ (in ohms)}}$

Here are some examples — the key here is choosing the **right equation** to use. If the question gives you the value of two variables and asks you to find a third, you should choose the equation that relates these three variables. You might have to **rearrange** it before using it.

EXAMPLE: What is the power output of a component with resistance 100 Ω if the current through it is 0.2 A?

$P = I^2R$, so $P = 0.2^2 \times 100 = $ **4 W**

EXAMPLE: Resistors get hotter when a current flows through them. If you double the current through a resistor, what happens to the amount of heat energy produced every second?

It **increases by a factor of 4** — this is because the current is squared in the expression for the power (you can substitute some values of I and R in to check this).

EXAMPLE: If a lamp has an operating power of 6.5 W and the potential difference across it is 12 V, what is its resistance?

$P = \frac{V^2}{R}$, so multiplying both sides by R gives $P \times R = V^2$, and dividing by P gives:

$R = \frac{V^2}{P}$, so $R = \frac{12^2}{6.5} = 22.153... = $ **22 Ω (to 2 s.f.)**

(This answer is rounded to 2 s.f. to match the data in the question — see page 1.)

Watts up with your watch, Dr Watson? Dunno, but it sure is i²rksome...

1) What is the power output of a 2400 Ω component if the current through it is 1.2 A?
2) A motor has a resistance of 100 Ω. How much work does it do in 1 minute if it is connected to a 6 V power supply?
3) The current through a 6.0 W lamp is 0.50 A. What is the resistance of the lamp?

Waves

Waves Transfer Energy Without Transferring Matter

1) Waves are **oscillations** that transfer energy — like water waves or electromagnetic waves.
2) Waves carry **energy** from one place to another **without** transferring **matter**.

Transverse Waves Vibrate at 90° to the Direction of Travel

Transverse waves have **vibrations** at **90°** to the direction of **energy transfer** and **travel**.
E.g. **electromagnetic** waves (like light) or shaking a Slinky® spring from side to side.

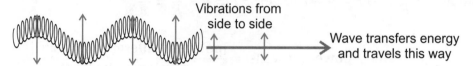

Vibrations from side to side

Wave transfers energy and travels this way

Longitudinal Waves Vibrate Along the Direction of Travel

Longitudinal waves vibrate in the **same direction** as the direction of **energy transfer** and **travel**.
They are made of alternate **compressions** and **rarefactions** of the medium.
E.g. sound waves or pushing on the end of a Slinky® spring.

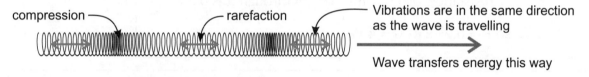

compression — rarefaction

Vibrations are in the same direction as the wave is travelling

Wave transfers energy this way

You Can Show Wave Motion on a Graph

A **displacement-distance** graph shows **how far** each part of the wave is **displaced** from its **equilibrium position** for different distances along the wave.

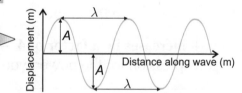

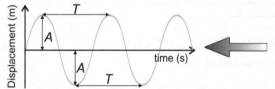

You can also consider **just one point** on a wave and plot how its **displacement** changes with **time**. This is a **displacement-time** graph.

> **Displacement** = how far a point on the wave has moved from its equilibrium position
> **Amplitude (A)** = the largest possible displacement from the equilibrium position
> **Wavelength (λ)** = the length of one wave cycle, from crest to crest or trough to trough
> **Period (T)** = the time taken for a whole cycle (vibration) to complete, or to pass a given point

Transverse waves are terrible singers — they always skip the chorus...

1) Sketch a graph of displacement against distance for five full wavelengths of a wave with amplitude 0.01 metres and wavelength 0.02 metres.
2) Sketch a graph of displacement against time for three complete oscillations of one part of a wave of amplitude 0.05 metres and time period 0.8 seconds.

Frequency and the Wave Equation

Frequency is the Number of Oscillations per Second

If a wave has a **time period** of 0.2 seconds, it takes 0.2 seconds for a point on the wave to complete **one full oscillation**. So in one second the point will complete **5 full oscillations**.

The number of oscillations that one point on a wave completes every second is called the **frequency** of the wave. It has the symbol *f* and is measured in **hertz** (Hz).

So a wave with a time period of 0.2 seconds has a **frequency** of 5 hertz.

The equation for frequency is:

$$\text{Frequency} = \frac{1}{\text{time period}} \quad \text{or} \quad f = \frac{1}{T}$$

EXAMPLE: A wave has a frequency of 350 Hz. What is the period of oscillation of one point on that wave?

$$T = \frac{1}{f} = \frac{1}{350} = 0.002857... = \textbf{0.0029 s (to 2 s.f.)}$$

The Wave Equation Relates Speed, Frequency and Wavelength

For a wave of **frequency** *f* (in hertz), **wavelength** λ (in metres) and **wave speed** *v* (in metres per second) the wave equation is:

$$\textbf{speed = frequency × wavelength} \quad \text{or} \quad v = f \times \lambda$$

EXAMPLE: Sound is a longitudinal wave. If a sound with a frequency of 250 Hz has a wavelength of 1.32 metres in air, what is the speed of sound in air?

$v = f \times \lambda = 250 \times 1.32 = \textbf{330 ms}^{-1}$

EXAMPLE: All electromagnetic waves travel at 3.0×10^8 ms^{-1} in a vacuum. If a radio wave has a wavelength of 1.5 km in a vacuum, what is its frequency?

$v = f \times \lambda$, so $f = \frac{v}{\lambda} = \frac{3.0 \times 10^8}{1.5 \times 10^3} = \textbf{200 000 Hz}$ (or 200 kHz)

Wave equation: lift arm + oscillate hand = pleasant non-vocal greeting...

1) A radio wave has a frequency of 6.25×10^5 Hz. What is the time period of the radio wave?
2) A sound wave has a time period of 0.0012 s. Find the frequency of the sound.
3) A wave along a spring has a frequency of 3.5 Hz and a wavelength of 1.4 m. What is the speed of the wave?
4) A wave has time period 7.1 s and is moving at speed 180 ms^{-1}.
   a) What is the frequency of the wave?
   b) What is the wavelength of the wave?

Superposition of Waves

Superposition Happens When Two Waves Meet

1) If two waves meet (e.g. waves on a rope travelling in opposite directions), their displacements will briefly **combine**.

2) They become **one single wave**, with a **displacement** equal to the displacement of each individual wave **added together**.

3) This is called **superposition**.

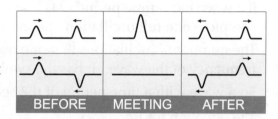

BEFORE   MEETING   AFTER

4) If two **crests** meet, the **heights** of the waves are **added together** and the crest height **increases**. This is called **constructive interference** because the **amplitude** of the superposed waves is **larger** than the amplitude of the individual waves.

5) If the **crest** of one wave meets the **trough** of another wave, you **subtract** the trough **depth** from the crest **height**. So if the crest height is **the same** as the trough depth they'll **cancel out**. This is called **destructive interference** because the **amplitude** of the superposed waves is **smaller** than that of the individual waves.

6) After combining, the waves then carry on **as they were** before.

If Waves are In Phase they Interfere Constructively

1) Two waves travelling in the **same direction** are **in phase** with each other when the **peaks** of one wave **exactly line up** with the **peaks** of the **other**, and the **troughs** of one wave **exactly line up** with the **troughs** of the **other**.

2) If these waves are **superposed**, they **interfere constructively**. The **combined amplitude** of the final wave is equal to the **sum** of the individual waves.

In phase, constructive interference

If Waves are Out of Phase they Interfere Destructively

1) Two waves are **exactly out of phase** if the **peaks** of one wave line up with the **troughs** of the other (and vice versa).

2) If these waves are **superposed**, they **interfere destructively**. If the individual waves had the same amplitude originally, they will **cancel each other out**.

Out of phase, destructive interference

Constructive interference — getting woken up early by noisy builders...

1) What is meant by:
   a) superposition?
   b) constructive interference?
   c) destructive interference?

2) A wave with an amplitude of 0.67 mm is superposed with an identical wave with the same amplitude. The waves are in phase. What is the amplitude of the superposed wave?

3) Two waves, both of amplitude 19.1 m, are exactly out of phase. What is the amplitude of the single wave formed when they superpose?

4) A wave with an amplitude of 35 cm is in phase with a 41 cm amplitude wave. The waves meet and constructive interference occurs. What is the amplitude of the combined wave?

Reflection and Diffraction

Waves can be *Reflected*

1) When a wave hits a **boundary** between one medium and another, some (or nearly all) of the wave is **reflected back**.

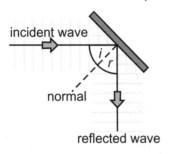

incident wave

normal

reflected wave

2) The angle of the **incident** (incoming) wave is called the **angle of incidence**, and the angle of the **reflected** wave is called the **angle of reflection.**

3) The angles of incidence and reflection are both **measured from the normal** — an imaginary line running **perpendicular** to the **boundary**.

4) The **law of reflection** says that:

angle of incidence (*i*) = angle of reflection (*r*)

Diffraction — Waves Spreading Out

1) Waves **spread out** ('**diffract**') at the edges when they pass through a **gap** or **pass an object**.

2) The **amount** of diffraction depends on the **size** of the gap relative to the **wavelength** of the wave. The **narrower the gap**, or the **longer the wavelength**, the more the wave spreads out.

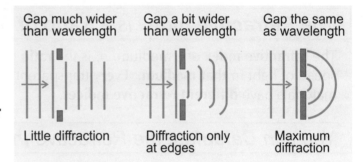

Gap much wider than wavelength — Little diffraction

Gap a bit wider than wavelength — Diffraction only at edges

Gap the same as wavelength — Maximum diffraction

3) A **narrow gap** is one about the same size as the **wavelength** of the wave. So whether a gap counts as narrow or not depends on the wave.

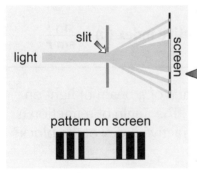

slit

light

screen

pattern on screen

4) If light is shone at a **narrow slit** about the **same width** as the **wavelength** of the light, the light **diffracts**.

5) The diffracted light forms a **diffraction pattern** of **bright** and **dark fringes**. This pattern is caused by **constructive** and **destructive interference** of light waves (see p.34).

6) You get diffraction around the edges of **obstacles** too.

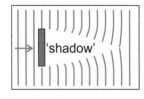

'shadow'

7) The **shadow** is where the wave is **blocked**. The **wider** the obstacle compared to the **wavelength**, the **less diffraction** it causes, so the **longer** the shadow.

Mind the gap between the train and the platform — you might diffract...

1) What is the law of reflection?

2) Sketch a diagram of a light wave being reflected at an angle by a mirror. Label the incident and reflected waves, the normal, the angle of incidence and the angle of reflection.

3) A water wave travels through a gap about as wide as its wavelength. The gap is made slightly larger. How will the amount of diffraction change?

4) What happens when light is shone at a slit about the same size as its wavelength?

Refraction

Waves can be Refracted

1) Reflection isn't all that happens when a wave meets a boundary. Usually, some of it is **refracted** too — it passes through the boundary and **changes direction**.

2) Waves travel at **different speeds** in **different media**.
E.g. — electromagnetic waves, like light, usually travel slower in denser media.

If a wave hits a boundary 'face on', it **slows down** without changing direction.

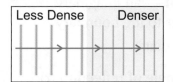

But if the wave hits at an angle, this bit **slows down first**...

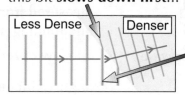

...while this bit carries on at the same speed until it meets the boundary. The wave **changes direction**.

When an electromagnetic wave enters a **denser** medium, it bends **towards** the normal. When one enters a **less dense** medium, it bends **away** from the normal.

The Refractive Index is a Ratio of Speeds

The **refractive index** of a medium, n, is the **ratio** of the speed of light in a **vacuum** to the speed of light in **that medium**. **Every** transparent material has a refractive index and different materials have **different refractive indices**.

You can Calculate the Refractive Index using Snell's Law

When an **incident ray** travelling in **air** meets a boundary with **another material**, the **angle of refraction** of the ray, r, depends on the **refractive index** of the material and the **angle of incidence**, i.

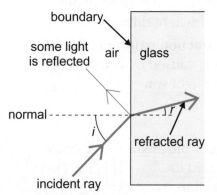

This is called **Snell's Law**.

refractive index $(n) = \dfrac{\sin i}{\sin r}$

> **EXAMPLE:** The angle of incidence of a beam of light on a glass block is 65°. The angle of refraction is 35°. What is the refractive index of the block?
>
> $n = \dfrac{\sin i}{\sin r} = \dfrac{\sin 65}{\sin 35} = 1.580... = \mathbf{1.6}$

You can **rearrange** Snell's Law to find an angle of refraction or incidence, e.g. $r = \sin^{-1}(\frac{\sin i}{n})$.

This page has a high refractive index — it's really slowed me down...

1) A wave hits a boundary between two media head on. Describe what happens to the wave.

2) A wave hits a boundary between two media at an angle. Describe what happens to the wave.

3) A light wave travelling in air hits a transparent material at an angle of 72° to the normal to the boundary. The angle of refraction is 39°. What is the refractive index of the material?

4) A light wave hits the surface of the water in a pond at 23° to the normal. The refractive index of the pond water is 1.3. What is the angle of refraction?

Atomic Structure

Atoms are *Made Up* of *Three* Types of *Particle*

1) According to the **nuclear model**, the atom is made up of electrons, protons and neutrons.

2) The **nucleus** is at the **centre** of the atom. It contains **protons** (which have a **positive** charge) and **neutrons** (which have **no charge**), giving the nucleus an **overall positive charge**. Protons and neutrons are both known as **nucleons**.

3) The nucleus is **tiny** but it makes up **most** of the **mass** of the atom. The rest of the atom is mostly **empty space**, containing only the negative **electrons** which orbit **around** the nucleus.

Here's the structure of a **lithium atom**:

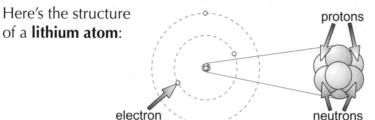

	relative mass	relative charge
proton	1	+1
neutron	1	0
electron	0.0005	−1

Atomic Structure can be *Represented* Using *Nuclide Notation*

1) The **proton number** (or atomic number), **Z**, is the number of **protons** in an atom.

2) The **nucleon number** (or mass number), **A**, is the total number of **protons** and **neutrons**.

3) An element can be **described** by its **proton** and **nucleon numbers**:

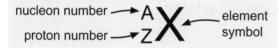

For example, lithium has 4 neutrons and 3 protons, so its symbol is ^7_3Li.

Isotopes are *Different Forms* of the *Same Element*

1) Isotopes are atoms with the **same number** of **protons** but a **different number** of **neutrons**.

2) This means they have the **same proton number**, but **different nucleon numbers**.

3) Many isotopes are **unstable** and give off **radiation** (see next page).

EXAMPLE: Carbon-12 and carbon-14 are two isotopes of carbon.

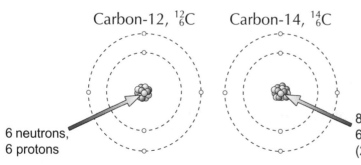

Carbon-12, $^{12}_6C$ Carbon-14, $^{14}_6C$

The radioactive decay of carbon-14 is used in radiocarbon dating to estimate the age of things that are thousands of years old.

6 neutrons, 6 protons

8 neutrons, 6 protons (2 extra neutrons)

Radiocarbon dating — what physicists do on Valentine's Day...

1) How many protons and neutrons are there in each of the following nuclei?
   a) $^{241}_{95}Am$ b) $^{239}_{94}Pu$ c) $^{90}_{38}Sr$ d) $^{60}_{27}Co$ e) $^{226}_{88}Ra$

2) What is an isotope of an element?

Nuclear Radiation

If an atom is **unstable**, it can undergo **radioactive decay** and give off **nuclear radiation**. By decaying, a nucleus emits **particles** or **energy**, making it **more stable**.

There are **three** kinds of nuclear radiation you need to know about:

In **Alpha Decay** (Symbol α), an Alpha Particle is Emitted

1) An **alpha particle** is emitted from the **nucleus**. It is made up of **two protons** and **two neutrons**.

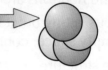

2) As a result, the **proton number** of the atom that has decayed goes **down by 2** and the **nucleon number** goes **down by 4**.

> **EXAMPLE:** The alpha decay of radium-226.
>
> $$^{226}_{88}Ra \rightarrow \, ^{222}_{86}Rn + \, ^{4}_{2}\alpha$$
>
> Proton and nucleon numbers are both conserved during all forms of radioactive decay:
>
> Nucleon number: $226 = 222 + 4$ Proton number: $88 = 86 + 2$

In **Beta Decay** (Symbol β), an **Electron** is Emitted

1) A **neutron** in the nucleus turns into a **proton** and an **electron**. The electron is **emitted** from the nucleus and is called a **beta particle**.

2) As a result the **proton number** of the nucleus goes **up by 1**, but the **nucleon number doesn't change**.

> **EXAMPLE:** The beta decay of radium-228.
>
> $$^{228}_{88}Ra \rightarrow \, ^{228}_{89}Ac + \, ^{0}_{-1}\beta$$
>
> Nucleon number: $228 = 228 + 0$
> Proton number: $88 = 89 - 1$

Gamma Decay (Symbol γ) Emits **Electromagnetic** Radiation

1) High-energy **electromagnetic radiation**, called **gamma radiation** is **emitted** from the nucleus.

2) The **number** of **protons** and **neutrons** in the nucleus **stays the same**.

> **EXAMPLE:** The gamma decay of iodine-131.
>
> $$^{131}_{53}I \rightarrow \, ^{131}_{53}I + \, ^{0}_{0}\gamma$$
>
> Proton and nucleon numbers don't change.

You beta learn this radiation stuff — I promise it's not alpha nothing...

1) What is an alpha particle made up of?

2) Describe what happens during the emission of beta and gamma radiation.

3) Complete the following decay equations by filling in any missing radiation symbols, proton numbers or nucleon numbers:

a) $^{242}_{94}Pu \rightarrow \, ^{}_{-}U + \, ^{4}_{2}\alpha$ b) $^{}_{-}K \rightarrow \, ^{40}_{20}Ca + \, ^{0}_{-1}\beta$ c) $^{222}_{86}Rn \rightarrow \, ^{218}_{84}Po + \, ^{}_{-}$ d) $^{14}_{6}C \rightarrow \, ^{}_{-}N + \, ^{0}_{-1}\beta$

Planning an Experiment and Collecting Data

Scientists do **Experiments** to **Answer Questions**

You need to **plan experiments** carefully to make sure you get the **best results** possible:

1) Make a **prediction** or **hypothesis** — a testable statement about what you think will happen.
2) Identify your **variables** (see below).
3) Think about any **risks**, and how you can minimise them.
4) Select the right **equipment** for the job — if you're measuring a time interval in minutes you might use a **stopwatch**, but if it's in milliseconds you may need to get a **computer** to measure the time for you, as your reaction time could interfere with your results.
5) Decide what **data** you need to collect and how you'll do it.
6) Write a clear, detailed **method** describing exactly what you're going to do.

You Need to Know What Your **Variables** Are

A variable is anything that has the **potential to change** in an experiment.

The **independent variable** is the thing **you change** in an experiment.	The **dependent variable** is the thing you **measure** in an experiment.

All the **other variables** must be kept the **same** to make it a **fair test**. These are **control variables**.

EXAMPLE: An experiment investigates how the height an object is dropped from affects the time it takes to fall. Identify the variables in this experiment.

The **independent variable** is the **height** you drop the object from — it's what you change. The **dependent variable** is the **time** the object takes to fall — it's what you measure. Everything else in the experiment should be **controlled**, so no other variables change. For example, the **same object** should be used throughout the experiment (so its size and mass don't change), the **conditions** in the room you do the experiment in should be constant, and you shouldn't change your measuring **equipment** halfway through.

Repeating an Experiment Lets You Calculate a **Mean**

Normally, you'll get a slightly different result every time you do an experiment, due to small **random errors** you can't control. E.g. — holding your head in a slightly different place each time you take a measurement from a ruler will cause random errors in the length you read off.

You can **reduce the effect** of these random errors on your results by **repeating** your experiment and taking an average, or **mean**, of your results.

To find the mean:
1) **Add together** the **results** of each repeat.
2) **Divide** this total by the number of **repeats** you did.

Independent variables — not keen on accepting help...

1) A scientist investigates how changing the potential difference across a circuit component affects the current through it. He measures the current three times at each potential difference.
   a) Identify the independent and dependent variables in this investigation.
   b) For a potential difference of 4 V, the scientist records currents of 0.13 A, 0.17 A and 0.12 A. Calculate the mean current through the component when the potential difference is 4 V.

Analysing Your Data

You can Present Your Results on a Graph

Graphs are the easiest way to see any **patterns** or **trends** in your results.

1) Usually the **independent variable** goes on the *x*-axis (along the bottom) and the **dependent variable** goes on the *y*-axis (up the side). Make sure you **label** both axes **clearly** with the quantity and **units**. Pick a **sensible scale** — both axes should go up in sensible steps, and should spread the data out over the full graph (rather than bunching it up in a corner).

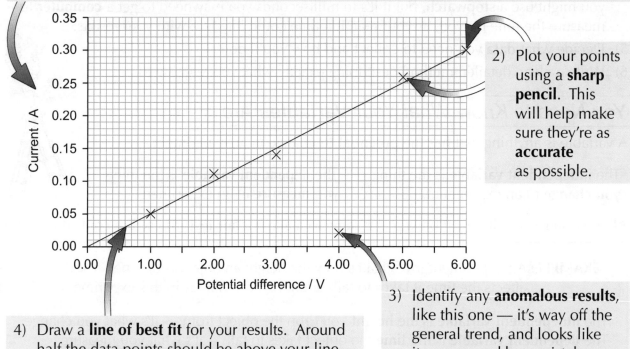

2) Plot your points using a **sharp pencil**. This will help make sure they're as **accurate** as possible.

3) Identify any **anomalous results**, like this one — it's way off the general trend, and looks like it was caused by a mistake. **Ignore** anomalous results when drawing your **line of best fit**.

4) Draw a **line of best fit** for your results. Around half the data points should be above your line of best fit and half below it. The line could be **straight** or **curved**, depending on your data.

Graphs Can Show Different Kinds of Correlation

The **correlation** describes the relationship between the variables. Data can show:

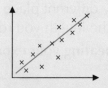

POSITIVE CORRELATION:
As one variable increases, the other increases.

NEGATIVE CORRELATION:
As one variable increases, the other decreases.

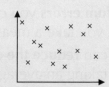

NO CORRELATION:
No relationship between the variables.

Remember, just because two variables are correlated it doesn't mean a change in one is **causing** a change in the other — there could be a third variable affecting them both.

Anomalouse results — unusual results in the insect breeding program...

1) The table on the right gives the speed of a cyclist as he accelerates from rest. Plot a graph of his speed against time, and draw a line of best fit.

time / s	0.0	2.0	4.0	6.0	8.0	10.0
speed / ms^{-1}	0.0	0.7	1.8	2.6	3.2	4.2

Conclusions and Uncertainty

*Draw **Conclusions** that Your Results **Support***

You should draw a conclusion that **explains** what your data shows.

1) Your conclusion should be limited to what you've **actually done** and found out in your experiment. For example, if you've been investigating how the force applied to a spring affects how much it stretches, and have only used forces between 0 and 5 N, you can't claim to know what would happen if you used a force of 10 N, or if you used a different spring.

2) You also need to think about how much you can **believe** your conclusion, by evaluating the **quality** of your results (see below). If you can't trust your results, you can't form a **strong conclusion**.

*You can Never Measure Anything **Exactly***

1) There will always be **errors** and **uncertainties** in your results caused by lots of different things, including **human error** (e.g. your reaction time). The more errors there are in your results, the **lower the quality** of your data. This will affect the strength of your **conclusion** (see above).

2) All measurements will have some uncertainty due to the equipment used. For example, if you measure a length with a ruler, you can only measure it to the nearest millimetre, as that's the **smallest difference** marked on the ruler's scale. If you measure a length with a ruler as 14 mm you can write this as **14 ± 0.5 mm** to show that you could be up to half a millimetre out either way.

3) If you have a value without a ± sign, the number of **significant figures** gives you an estimate of the **uncertainty**. For example, 72 ms^{-1} has **2 significant figures**, so without any other information you know this value must be 72 **± 0.5 ms^{-1}** — if the value was less than 71.5 ms^{-1} it would have been rounded to 71 ms^{-1}, if it was greater than 72.5 ms^{-1} it would have been rounded to 73 ms^{-1}.

*Think About How to **Improve** Your Experiment*

You should always think about how your experiment could be **improved**:

1) Did the experiment actually **test** what it was supposed to? Could you make it more **relevant** to the question?

2) Was there anything you could have done to prevent some of the **errors** in your results?

3) Would different **apparatus** or a different **method** have given you **better results**?

In conclusion, I need a cup of tea...

1) A student records how long it takes for a car to stop when the brakes are fully applied. He uses a stopwatch, and gets a measurement of 7.628 ± 0.0005 seconds.
   a) What is the smallest difference the stopwatch can measure?
   b) The student says from his result he can accurately report the time taken for the car to stop to 4 significant figures. Is he correct? Explain your answer.

Answers

N.B. — All numerical answers here have been rounded to the same number of significant figures as the given data value with the least number of significant figures (see page 1).

Section 1 — Forces and Motion

Page 2 — Speed, Displacement and Velocity

1 speed = distance ÷ time = $1500 \div 210 = 7.142...$
$$= \textbf{7.1 ms}^{-1} \textbf{ (to 2 s.f.)}$$

2 distance = speed × time = $(3.0 \times 10^8) \times (8.3 \times 60)$
$$= 1.494 \times 10^{11}$$
$$= \textbf{1.5} \times \textbf{10}^{11} \textbf{ m (to 2 s.f.)}$$

3 time = distance ÷ speed. 1.5 m = 150 cm,
so time = $150 \div 0.24 = 625 = \textbf{620 seconds (to 2 s.f.)}$

4 $t = s \div v = (1 \times 1000) \div 50 = \textbf{20 s}$

5 $s = v \times t = 7.50 \times 15.0 = 112.5$
$$= \textbf{113 m south (to 3 s.f.)}$$

Page 3 — Drawing Displacements and Velocities

1 a) ———————— 12 m ————————→
   b) ←———————— 110 miles ————————

2 a)

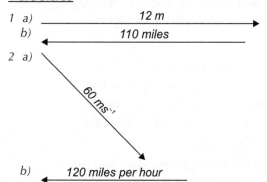

   b) ←———— 120 miles per hour ————

Page 4 — Combining Displacements and Velocities

1 a) By measuring:

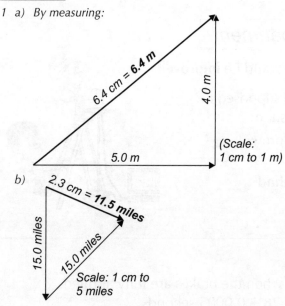

   b)

2 By measuring:

$$- \underset{3.0\ ms^{-1}}{\overset{1.0\ ms^{-1}}{\Big\uparrow}} \overset{1.0\ ms^{-1}}{\longleftarrow} = \underset{3.0\ ms^{-1}}{\overset{1.0\ ms^{-1}}{\Big\uparrow}} + \overset{1.0\ ms^{-1}}{\longrightarrow} = \underset{3.0\ ms^{-1}}{\Big\uparrow}\ \nearrow^{3.2\ ms^{-1}}_{3.2\ cm}$$

(Scale: 1 cm to 1 ms⁻¹)

Or by Pythagoras: $\Delta v = \sqrt{3.0^2 + 1.0^2} = 3.162...$
$$= \textbf{3.2 m (to 2 s.f.)}$$

Page 5 — Resolving Vectors

1 Horizontal component = $v_x = v \cos\theta = 12 \times \cos 68$
$$= 4.495... = \textbf{4.5 ms}^{-1} \textbf{ (to 2 s.f.)}$$
   Vertical component = $v_y = v \sin\theta = 12 \times \sin 68$
$$= 11.128... = \textbf{11 ms}^{-1} \textbf{ (to 2 s.f.)}$$

2 $\cos\theta = \frac{v_x}{v}$. Rearranging for θ gives:
$$\theta = \cos^{-1}\left(\frac{v_x}{v}\right) = \cos^{-1}\frac{67}{98} = 46.868...$$
$$= \textbf{47° (to 2 s.f.)}$$

3 Vertical velocity = $v_y = v \sin\theta = 5.9 \times \sin 23$
$$= 2.305...\ ms^{-1}$$
   Time taken to descend 150 m = $\frac{s}{v_y} = \frac{150}{2.305...}$
$$= 65.067...$$
$$= \textbf{65 s (to 2 s.f.)}$$

Page 6 — Acceleration

1 $u = 12.8\ ms^{-1}$ to the left $= -12.8\ ms^{-1}$
   $v = 18.3\ ms^{-1}$ to the right $= +18.3\ ms^{-1}$
$$a = \frac{v-u}{t} = \frac{18.3-(-12.8)}{22.0} = 1.4136...$$
$$= \textbf{1.41 ms}^{-2} \textbf{ to the right (to 2 s.f.)}$$

2 $t = \frac{v-u}{a} = \frac{4.5-1.5}{0.18} = 16.66... = \textbf{17 s (to 2 s.f.)}$

3 $u = v - (a \times t) = 0 - (-0.41 \times 3.7) = 1.517$
$$= \textbf{1.5 ms}^{-1} \textbf{ (to 2 s.f.)}$$

Page 7 — Acceleration Due To Gravity

1 $t = \frac{v-u}{a} = \frac{-4.9-0}{-9.81} = 0.4994... = \textbf{0.50 s (to 2 s.f.)}$

2 $u = v - (a \times t) = -26.5 - (-9.81 \times 2.15) = -5.4085$
$$= \textbf{5.41 ms}^{-1} \textbf{ downwards (to 3 s.f.)}$$

3 $v = u + (a \times t) = 0 + (-9.81 \times 10.0) = -98.1$
$$= \textbf{98.1 ms}^{-1} \textbf{ down}$$

4 $t = \frac{v-u}{a} = \frac{-24.5-0}{-9.81} = 2.4974... = \textbf{2.50 s (to 3 s.f.)}$

5 $u = v - (a \times t) = -10.7 - (-9.81 \times 1.90) = 7.939$
$$= \textbf{7.94 ms}^{-1} \textbf{ up (to 3 s.f.)}$$

Answers

Page 8 — Displacement-Time Graphs

1   E.g.
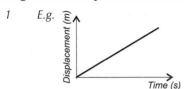

2   E.g.
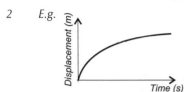

3   E.g.
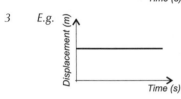

4   E.g.
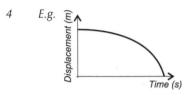

Page 9 — Displacement-Time Graphs

1   a) *It is accelerating (towards the start line).*
    b) *Between 3 and 4 seconds it is moving towards the start line and decelerating until it is stationary. It travels 20 metres in this time. Between 4 and 6 seconds it remains stationary zero metres from the start line.*
    c) *Velocity = (160 − 40) ÷ (10 − 8)*
        *= 120 ÷ 2 = **60 ms⁻¹***
    d) *Average velocity = (180 − 80) ÷ 14 = 100 ÷ 14*
        *= 7.1428... = **7 ms⁻¹ (to 1 s.f.)***
    e) *Average speed = (80 + 180) ÷ 14 = 260 ÷ 14*
        *= 18.571... = **20 ms⁻¹ (to 1 s.f.)***

Page 11 — Velocity-Time Graphs

1   a) *A (0 s-10 s), acceleration = $\frac{10-6}{10-0}$ = **0.4 ms⁻²**,*

        *B (10 s-20 s), acceleration = $\frac{10-10}{20-10}$ = **0 ms⁻²**,*

        *C (20 s-30 s), acceleration = $\frac{2-10}{30-20}$ = **−0.8 ms⁻²***

    b) *A (0 s-10 s), area = ½(6 + 10) × 10 = 80 m*
        B (10 s-20 s), area = 10 × 10 = 100 m
        C (20 s-30 s), area = ½(10 + 2) × 10 = 60 m
        *Total distance travelled = 80 + 100 + 60 = **240 m***

2   a) *A (0 s-3 s), acceleration = $\frac{15-0}{3-0}$ = **5 ms⁻²***

        *B (3 s-4 s), acceleration = $\frac{10-15}{4-3}$ = **−5 ms⁻²***

        *C (4 s-6 s), acceleration = $\frac{20-10}{6-4}$ = **5 ms⁻²***

    b) *A (0 s-3 s), area = ½ × 15 × 3 = 22.5 m*
        B (3 s-4 s), area = ½(15 + 10) × 1 = 12.5 m
        C (4 s-6 s), area = ½(10 + 20) × 2 = 30 m
        *Total distance travelled = 22.5 + 12.5 + 30 = **65 m***

Page 12 — Adding and Resolving Forces

1   a) *8 − 5 = **3 N to the right, forces are unbalanced**.*
    b) *700 − 200 = **500 N to the left, forces are unbalanced**.*
    c) *2 − 2 = **0 N, forces are balanced**.*

2
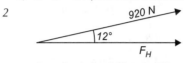

    $F_H = F \cos \theta = 920 \times \cos 12 = 899.89...$
    *= **900 N (to 2 s.f.)***

3   $F_V = F \sin \theta = 150 \times \sin 78 = 146.72...$
    *= **150 N (to 2 s.f.)***

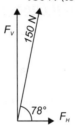

Page 14 — Forces and Acceleration

1   $F = m \times a = 840 \times 0.50 = **420 N**$

2   $F = m \times a = 0.120 \times 9.81 = 1.1772$
    *= **1.18 N (to 3 s.f.)***

3   $a = F \div m = 250 \div 0.5 = **500 ms⁻²**$

4   $m = F \div a = 55\,000 \div 0.275 = **200\,000 kg**$

5   $a = F \div m = 8600 \div 15\,000 = 0.573...\ ms⁻²$
    $a = \frac{v-u}{t}$, *so* $v = u + (a \times t) = 0 + (0.573... \times 25)$
        *= 14.333... = **14 ms⁻¹ (to 2 s.f.)***

Answers

Section 2 — Energy

Page 15 — Kinetic Energy

1 $E_k = \frac{1}{2} \times m \times v^2 = \frac{1}{2} \times 0.125 \times 72.0^2 =$ **324 J**

2 $E_k = \frac{1}{2} \times m \times v^2$ so $m = \frac{2 \times E_k}{v^2} = \frac{2 \times 5.4 \times 10^7}{15^2}$
   $= $ **4.8 × 10⁵ kg**

3 $v = \sqrt{\frac{2 \times E_k}{m}} = \sqrt{\frac{2 \times 1.0 \times 10^{-6}}{0.057}} = 5.9234... \times 10^{-3}$
   $= $ **5.9 × 10⁻³ ms⁻¹** *(or 0.59 cm s⁻¹) (to 2 s.f.)*

Page 16 — Gravitational Potential Energy

1 $E_p = m \times g \times h = 750 \times 9.81 \times 350 = 2\,575\,125$
   $= $ **2.6 × 10⁶ J** *(to 2 s.f.)*

2 $m = \frac{E_p}{g \times h} = \frac{1715}{9.81 \times 7.00} = 24.974... = $ **25.0 kg** *(to 3 s.f.)*

3 $h = \frac{E_p}{m \times g} = \frac{24\,700}{65.0 \times 9.81} = 38.735... = $ **38.7 m** *(to 3 s.f.)*

Page 17 — Conservation of Energy

1 E_k lost = E_p gained = 2850 J
   So $E_p = m \times g \times h = 2850$ J
   $m = \frac{E_p}{g \times h} = \frac{2850}{9.81 \times 5.10} = 56.964... = $ **57.0 kg** *(to 3 s.f.)*

2 E_p lost = $m \times g \times h = 0.475 \times 9.81 \times 0.920 = 4.28697$ J
   E_p lost = E_k gained, so $E_k = \frac{1}{2} \times m \times v^2 = 4.28697$ J
   $v = \sqrt{\frac{2 \times E_k}{m}} = \sqrt{\frac{2 \times 4.28697}{0.475}} = 4.2485...$
   $= $ **4.25 ms⁻¹** *(to 3 s.f.)*

3 E_k lost = $\frac{1}{2} \times m \times v^2 = \frac{1}{2} \times 0.015 \times 420^2 = 1323$ J
   E_p gained = E_k lost, so $E_p = m \times g \times h = 1323$ J
   $h = \frac{E_p}{m \times g} = \frac{1323}{0.015 \times 9.81} = 8990.8...$
   $= $ **9000 m** *(to 2 s.f.)*

Page 18 — Work

1 $W = F \times s = 25 \times 44 = $ **1100 J**

2 $W = F\cos\theta \times s = 17 \times \cos 35 \times 2.5 = 34.81...$
   $= $ **35 J** *(to 2 s.f.)*

Page 19 — Work

1 a) $W = F \times s = 125 \times 2.50 = 312.5 = $ **313 J** *(to 3 s.f.)*
  b) $E_p = m \times g \times h = 5.75 \times 9.81 \times 2.50 = 141.01...$
      $= $ **141 J** *(to 3 s.f.)*
  c) Work done = increase in E_k + increase in E_p so:
      $E_k = W - E_p = 312.5 - 141.01... = 171.48...$
      $= $ **171 J** *(to 3 s.f.)*
  d) $v = \sqrt{\frac{2 \times E_k}{m}} = \sqrt{\frac{2 \times 171.48...}{5.75}} = 7.7230...$
      $= $ **7.72 ms⁻¹** *(to 3 s.f.)*

Page 20 — Power

1 $P = \frac{W}{t} = \frac{250}{4.0} = 62.5 = $ **63 W** *(to 2 s.f.)*

2 $t = \frac{W}{P} = \frac{91 \times 1000}{14 \times 1000} = \frac{91\,000}{14\,000} = $ **6.5 s**

3 $W = F \times s = 276 \times (1.25 \times 1000) = 345\,000$ J
   $P = \frac{W}{t} = \frac{345\,000}{2.5 \times 60} = $ **2300 W**

Page 21 — Power

1 $P = F \times v = 1.80 \times 10^5 \times 40.0$
   $= $ **7.20 × 10⁶ W** *(or 7.20 MW)*

2 The skydiver's weight is equal to the force, F, exerted by gravity on her mass, so:
   $F = \frac{P}{v} = \frac{31\,500}{45} = $ **700 N**

3 $v = \frac{P}{F} = \frac{5.20 \times 10^4}{1650} = 31.515... = $ **31.5 ms⁻¹** *(to 3 s.f.)*

Page 22 — Efficiency

1 Useful energy out = $E_p = m \times g \times h$
   $= 12.9 \times 9.81 \times 2.50 = 316.3725$ J
   Efficiency = $\frac{\text{useful energy out}}{\text{total energy in}} \times 100\%$
   $= \frac{316.3725}{375} \times 100\% = 84.366 = $ **84.4%**

2 a) $E_k = \frac{1}{2} \times m \times v^2 = \frac{1}{2} \times 560 \times 25^2 = 1.75 \times 10^5$
      $= $ **1.8 × 10⁵ J** *(or 180 kJ) (to 2 s.f.)*
  b) Efficiency = $\frac{\text{useful energy out}}{\text{total energy in}} \times 100\%$
      $= \frac{1.75 \times 10^5}{1.4 \times 10^6} \times 100\% = 12.5$
      $= $ **13%** *(to 2 s.f.)*

Section 3 — Materials

Page 24 — Forces and Springs

1 $F = k \times \Delta l = 64.1 \times 0.245 = 15.7045$
   $= $ **15.7 N** *(to 3 s.f.)*

2 $\Delta l = \frac{F}{k} = \frac{378}{84.0} = $ **4.50 m**

3 a) $F = m \times g = 7.4 \times 9.81 = 72.594$ N
      $k = \frac{F}{\Delta l} = \frac{72.594}{0.084} = 864.214... = $ **860 Nm⁻¹** *(to 2 s.f.)*
  b) $F = k \times \Delta l = 864.214... \times 0.095 = 82.100...$ N
      $m = \frac{F}{g} = \frac{82.100...}{9.81} = 8.369... = $ **8.4 kg** *(to 2 s.f.)*
      Yes, the bag can be taken on the flight.

4 a) The maximum force at which an object's extension is still proportional to the force applied to it.
  b) It could have been stretched beyond its elastic limit.

Answers

Section 4 — Electricity

Page 25 — Current and Potential Difference

1   $I = \frac{Q}{t}$, so $t = \frac{Q}{I} = \frac{12}{3.0} = \textbf{4.0 s}$

2   $V = \frac{W}{Q}$, so $W = V \times Q = 1.5 \times 9.2 = \textbf{13.8 V}$

3   $I = \frac{Q}{t}$, so $Q = I \times t = 3.80 \times 275 = 1045$ C

   $V = \frac{W}{Q} = \frac{9540}{1045} = 9.129... = \textbf{9.13 V (to 3 s.f.)}$

Page 26 — Current in Electric Circuits

1   $0.5 = I_1 + 0.2 + 0.05$
   $0.5 = I_1 + 0.25$
   $I_1 = 0.5 - 0.25$
   $I_1 = \textbf{0.25 A}$

2   $0.4 + 0.3 + I_2 = 1.3$
   $0.7 + I_2 = 1.3$
   $I_2 = 1.3 - 0.7$
   $I_2 = \textbf{0.6 A}$

Page 27 — Potential Difference in Electric Circuits

1 a) $12 = V_M + 3$
      $V_M = 12 - 3$
         $= \textbf{9 V}$
   b) $12 = 6 + 2 + V_S$
      $V_S = 12 - 6 - 2$
         $= \textbf{4 V}$

2   **12 V**

Page 28 — Resistance

1   $V = I \times R$, so $V = 2.5 \times 15 = 37.5 = \textbf{38 V (to 2 s.f.)}$

2   $I = \frac{V}{R} = \frac{6.0}{2500} = \textbf{0.0024 A}$ (or 2.4 mA)

3   $R = \frac{V}{I} = \frac{1.5}{0.024} = 62.5 = \textbf{63 }\Omega\textbf{ (to 2 s.f.)}$

Page 29 — I-V Graphs

1   *Provided the temperature is constant, the current though an ohmic component is directly proportional to the potential difference across it (V = IR).*

2 a)
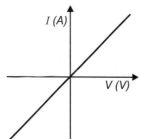

b)
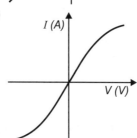

c)
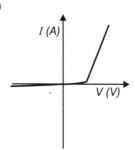

Page 30 — Power in Circuits

1   $P = V \times I = 6.5 \times 0.12 = \textbf{0.78 W}$

2 a) $I = \frac{P}{V} = \frac{45}{14} = 3.214... = \textbf{3.2 A (to 2 s.f.)}$
  b) $W = P \times t = 45 \times 12 = \textbf{540 J}$

Page 31 — Power in Circuits

1   $P = I^2R = 1.2^2 \times 2400 = 3456 = \textbf{3500 W (to 2 s.f.)}$

2   $P = \frac{V^2}{R} = \frac{6^2}{100} = \frac{36}{100} = 0.36$ W
   $W = P \times t = 0.36 \times 60 = 21.6 = \textbf{20 J (to 1 s.f.)}$

3   $R = \frac{P}{I^2} = \frac{6.0}{0.50^2} = \textbf{24 }\Omega$

Answers

Section 5 — Waves

Page 32 — Waves

1 E.g.

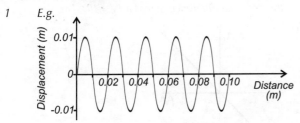

2 E.g.

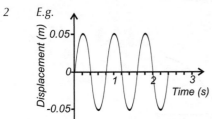

Page 33 — Frequency and the Wave Equation

1 $T = \dfrac{1}{f} = \dfrac{1}{6.25 \times 10^5} = \mathbf{1.60 \times 10^{-6}\ s}$

2 $f = \dfrac{1}{T} = \dfrac{1}{0.0012} = 833.33... = \mathbf{830\ Hz\ (to\ 2\ s.f.)}$

3 $v = f \times \lambda = 3.5 \times 1.4 = \mathbf{4.9\ ms^{-1}}$

4 a) $f = \dfrac{1}{T} = \dfrac{1}{7.1} = 0.1408... = \mathbf{0.14\ Hz\ (to\ 2\ s.f.)}$

   b) $v = f \times \lambda$, so $\lambda = \dfrac{v}{f} = \dfrac{180}{0.1408...} = 1278$
$$= \mathbf{1300\ m\ (to\ 2\ s.f.)}$$

Page 34 — Superposition of Waves

1 a) If two waves meet they will briefly combine and become one single wave, with a displacement equal to the displacement of each individual wave added together.

   b) When the amplitude of the combined wave is larger than the amplitude of the individual waves.

   c) When the amplitude of the combined wave is smaller than the amplitude of the individual waves.

2 Amplitude = 0.67 + 0.67 = **1.34 mm**

3 The waves will cancel each other out completely, so the amplitude will be **0 m**.

4 Amplitude = 35 + 41 = **76 cm**

Page 35 — Reflection and Diffraction

1 Angle of incidence (i) = angle of reflection (r)

2 E.g.

incident wave — mirror — i r — normal — reflected wave

3 When the gap is about the same size as the wavelength, there will be a lot of diffraction. When the gap is made slightly larger, the amount of diffraction will decrease.

4 Light diffracts as it passes through the slit and forms a diffraction pattern of light and dark fringes.

Page 36 — Refraction

1 The wave slows down without changing direction.

2 The wave slows down and changes direction.

3 $n = \dfrac{\sin i}{\sin r} = \dfrac{\sin 72}{\sin 39} = 1.511... = \mathbf{1.5}$

4 $n = \dfrac{\sin i}{\sin r}$ so $\sin r = \dfrac{\sin i}{n} = \dfrac{\sin 23}{1.3} = 0.3005...$
so $r = \sin^{-1} 0.3005... = 17.49... = \mathbf{17°\ (to\ 2\ s.f.)}$

Section 6 — Atoms and Radioactivity

Page 37 — Atomic Structure

1 a) 95 protons, 146 neutrons

   b) 94 protons, 145 neutrons

   c) 38 protons, 52 neutrons

   d) 27 protons, 33 neutrons

   e) 88 protons, 138 neutrons

2 An isotope is a different form of the same element. It has the same number of protons but a different number of neutrons.

Page 38 — Nuclear Radiation

1 An alpha particle is made up of two protons and two neutrons.

2 In beta radiation a neutron in the nucleus turns into a proton and an electron. The electron is emitted from the nucleus.
In gamma radiation high-energy electromagnetic radiation is emitted from the nucleus. There is no change to the number of protons and neutrons.

3 a) $^{242}_{94}Pu \rightarrow \ ^{238}_{92}U + \ ^{4}_{2}\alpha$

   b) $^{40}_{19}K \rightarrow \ ^{40}_{20}Ca + \ ^{0}_{-1}\beta$

   c) $^{222}_{86}Rn \rightarrow \ ^{218}_{84}Po + \ ^{4}_{2}\alpha$

   d) $^{14}_{6}C \rightarrow \ ^{14}_{7}N + \ ^{0}_{-1}\beta$

Answers

Section 7 — Investigating and Interpreting

Page 39 — Planning an Experiment and Collecting Data

1 a) Independent variable: potential difference across the component.
   Dependent variable: current through the component.

 b) $(0.13 + 0.17 + 0.12) \div 3 = 0.14$ A

Page 40 — Analysing Your Data

1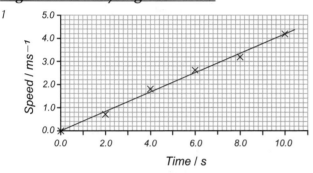

Page 41 — Conclusions and Uncertainty

1 a) 0.001 s (or 1 ms)

 b) No. There will be some human error in the result caused by the student's reaction time.

48

Index

A
acceleration 6–11, 13, 14
  due to gravity 7
alpha decay 38
amplitude 32
anomalous results 40
atomic structure 37
atoms 37, 38
averages 39

B
beta decay 38

C
charge 25, 26
circuits 25–27, 30, 31
combining vectors 4
conclusions 41
conservation of charge 26
conservation of energy 17, 27
constructive interference 34, 35
control variables 39
conventional current 25
correlation 40
current 25, 26, 28, 29, 31

D
dependent variables 39
destructive interference 34, 35
diffraction 35
diodes 29
displacement 2–4, 8, 9
  combining displacements 4
  waves 32
displacement-time graphs 8, 9
distance 2, 9, 10

E
efficiency 22
elastic limit 24
elastic strain energy 24
electricity 25–31
  circuits 25–27, 30, 31
  current 25, 26, 28, 29, 31
  I-V graphs 29
  potential difference 25, 27–31
  power 30, 31
  resistance 28, 29, 31
electrons 37
  as current 25
  beta decay 38
energy 15–22
  conservation of energy 17, 27
  efficiency 22
  elastic strain energy 24
  gravitational potential energy 16
  in circuits 27
  kinetic energy 15
  power 20, 21
  work 18–21
errors 39, 41

F
filament lamps 29
forces 12–14, 18, 19, 21
  on springs 23, 24
  resolving forces 12
  resultant forces 12–14
frequency 33

G
gamma decay 38
graphs 40
  displacement-time graphs 8, 9
  force-extension graphs 24
  I-V graphs 29
  velocity-time graphs 10, 11
gravitational potential energy 16
gravity 7

H
Hooke's law 23, 24
hypotheses 39

I
independent variables 39
index notation 1
interference
  constructive 34, 35
  destructive 34, 35
isotopes 37
I-V graphs 29

K
kinetic energy 15
Kirchoff's laws 26, 27

L
limit of proportionality 24
lines of best fit 40
longitudinal waves 32

N
negative correlation 40
neutrons 37
Newton's laws of motion 13, 14
nuclear radiation 38
nucleon numbers 37, 38
nucleons 37
nuclide notation 37

O
Ohm's law 29

P
phase 34
planning experiments 39
plastic deformation 24
positive correlation 40
potential difference 25, 27–31
power 20, 21, 30, 31
proton numbers 37, 38
protons 37
Pythagoras' theorem 4

R
radiation 38
radioactive decay 38
random errors 39
reflection 35
refraction 36
refractive indices 36
resistance 28, 29, 31
resultant forces 12–14
resultant vectors 4

S
scale drawings 3
significant figures 1, 41
Snell's law 36
speed 2
  of a wave 33
spring constants 23
springs 23, 24
standard form 1
superposition 34
symbols 1

T
time period 32, 33
transverse waves 32
trigonometry 5, 18, 36

U
uncertainties 41
units 1

V
variables 39
vectors 2–5, 12
  resolving 5, 12
  resultant 4
velocity 2–6, 8–11
  combining velocities 4
velocity-time graphs 10
voltage 25, 27–31

W
wavelength 32, 33, 35
waves 32–36
  diffraction 35
  frequency 33
  graphs 32
  longitudinal 32
  reflection 35
  refraction 36
  speed 33
  superposition 34
  time period 32, 33
  transverse 32
  wave equation 33
work 18–21